PRAISE FOR

THE HEART OF HOSPICE

"Every generation or so, an event comes along that challenges the way we look at sickness and death, and requires those of us who work in the medical field to reexamine how we care for our patients, and how we should best prepare them and their loved ones for the end of life. I've witnessed two of these transformative, worldwide moments in my medical career; the AIDS epidemic of the 1980s, and the COVID-19 pandemic of today. In both cases we saw sickness and death on a mass scale, where healthy people in the prime of their lives were suddenly gravely ill or dying within weeks. We also saw how devastating it can be for patients to die without human contact, unable to feel the touch and presence of their caretakers and loved ones.

The Heart of Hospice reminds us how important it is for the dying to experience touch, human connection and dignity at the end of life. Through the journey of one hospice patient from beginning to end, Ms. Whalen gracefully illustrates that these compassionate connections are absolutely integral to letting go peacefully. Drawing on personal experiences over her forty-year nursing career, Aimee has outlined an enlightened but practical approach to patient care that seamlessly blends traditional western medical care with holistic teachings such as Reiki and Therapeutic / Healing Touch, all to the benefit of both the patient and their families. Her book also makes a compelling argument that an early referral to a professional hospice organization often results in a more peaceful, dignified, fulfilling end of life experience.

The Heart of Hospice should be required reading for medical residents on their hospice and palliative care rotations. But whether you're in the medical field, you know someone who's sick, or you just want a better understanding of life's final chapter, this book should give us all an ending to strive for."

Dr. Louis J Avvento MD,
Board Certified Hospice & Palliative Care Medicine;
Internal Medicine and Medical Director of East End Hospice

"Hospice is a very often misunderstood concept. When most people hear the word hospice, they think it refers to a specific place and liken it to giving up the fight. In this work, Ms. Whalen portrays what the hospice experience can look like; she demystifies what hospice is and how meaningful an experience it can be for a patient and family. What stands out here is the individualized care provided by a team of professionals to ensure that there is quality, dignity, and humanity at the end of life. Working in hospice in different facets for over 15 years as a Licensed Clinical Social Worker it is easy to highly recommend *The Heart of Hospice* to both clinicians and laypeople as Ms. Whalen's kindness and compassion shine through in her effort to reframe and get to the core of what it truly means to be a hospice patient."

Angela Byrns, LCSW, Child's Bereavement Coordinator

"I have known Aimee Whalen for over 30 years as a friend, colleague, and have had the honor to be her mentor in her studies of Energy Healing. I have also been blessed to be a witness in her practice with patients, her service, integrity, love, compassion, and devotion that always graces her abilities in the healing arts. I recommend her highly, and whoever is in her care is truly blessed. We all can be thankful and grateful for Aimee's book: *The Heart of Hospice* is a generous and beautiful book about a subject that is so difficult to talk about, however; Aimee does, in her unique kind way!"

Dr. Linda Lancaster, author of *Harmonic Healing*

"Following the journey of one family facing the end of life of a loved one, *The Heart of Hospice* is a beautiful book to deeply understand the gift of hospice. Aimee Whalen, a nurse for 40 years, writes from her heart. In this story, with tenderness and compassion, she shares the many experiences and possibilities that hospice offers that benefits and supports the people they serve. This book personally touches us with the importance of being together and guided at the times of significant health challenges and end of life. Thank you, Aimee, for sharing with us your passion to help and comfort others and the Hospice organizations everywhere for all that you do to support those of us who need you."

Susan Steiner, Upledger Institute in CranioSacral Therapy

"As The Natural Nurse®, I am deeply involved in many aspects of natural health. When I interviewed Nurse Aimee Whalen on my radio show, I was delighted to have her share her personal and powerful experiences on how compassion and subtle energies are the pathways to ultimate health. Grounded in scientific rigor, Nurse Aimee explores an expanded approach to the healing arts, while recognizing the true nature of the complexity of life in her book, *The Heart of Hospice*. She integrates her vast knowledge base to bring the reader an in-depth understanding of a wonderful, supportive path for end-of-life care. The book is beautifully illustrated and offers practical guidance for decisions faced at the most difficult of times. Aimee offers a platform from a nursing standpoint. It is a guide for all nurses and provides comfort for family and caregivers at the end-of-life and includes the important role of prayer and spirituality for the patients and caregivers as well. This book is a supportive, practical, and inspiring guide for anyone who helps others cross the precipice."

Ellen Kamhi, radio host of "The Natural Nurse"
naturalnurse.com

"As human beings, we all hope; whether it be for a sunny day to go to the beach, to have a successful business, or to hope our children are well and happy. Hope continues for those individuals who are forced to face the news that their illness is no longer curable. At this time, hope may come in a different form. Hospice is a key component in helping patients reset their desired hopes; from being free of illness to hopes which may include the hope to be pain-free, to develop new memories with family and friends, or the hope to say final goodbyes to loved ones. *The Heart of Hospice* written by Aimee Whalen simply and beautifully captures the forms which hope may take as individuals and their families begin to craft their unimaginable new expectations in their lives. As a hospice nurse practitioner for over 15 years, I highly recommend Ms. Whalen's book for lay people as well as clinicians."

Marianne Gelber, MSN, Advanced Certified Hospice Nurse

KINDLE DIRECT PUBLISHING

The Heart of Hospice

Copyright @ 2021 by Aimee Whalen
All rights reserved

Kindle Direct Publishing
Visit our Web site at www.kdp.amazon.com

Printed in the United States of America

First Trade Printing December 2021

The Library of Congress has cataloged the hardcover edition as
follows:

Library of Congress Cataloging-in-Publication Data

Whalen, Aimee
The Heart of Hospice
ISBN…9798783581304

Edited by Danny Whalen

Cover by Andrea Shine

Illustrations by Lucy Reyer

THE HEART OF

HOSPICE

AIMEE WHALEN RN, BSN

CONTENTS

Preface

Why I Wrote This Book

I received my BSN from Catholic University in 1981, at the same time that the art of natural healing was taught at the collegiate level. The pioneers of healing by touch were Dolores Krieger and Dora Kunz who adopted the *laying on of hands* approach to healing.

I spent 20 years of a 40+ year career in various aspects of pediatrics. The late 1980s saw the rise of the AIDS epidemic. It hit the children of the poor hard. The babies born to HIV infected mothers had a chance if they received proper care. With my experience in Pediatric ICU and home-care, I cared for these medically fragile children with all the tools and medicines Western medicine could provide; however, I also expanded my knowledge and work in the areas of palliative care and infant massage. I endeavored to learn to heal the body and mind, as well as the soul, of the afflicted and their families.

A chance encounter on a return flight from vacation brought me to know Dr. Linda Lancaster, the founder of Light Harmonics Institute; a healing and teaching center specializing in energy medicine based in Santa Fe, New Mexico. Dr. Linda imparted her belief that virtually anyone with the right care could get to a better place. A diagnosis of Crohn's disease in my young nephew motivated me further to complete Dr. Linda's program.

In 2004 I received a Master's Degree in Medical Radiesthesia and Radionics. I went on to also become a Reiki Master, Biofeedback Specialist, Compassionate/Therapeutic Touch Therapist and Craniosacral Therapist. I hold certifications in Spiritual Healing and Pangu Medical Shengong and Vibrational Sound Therapy with Tibetan singing bowls. I am a long-time member of the International Order of St. Luke's The Physician.

From the adolescent unit in The Bronx and the more impoverished neighborhoods of Guatemala and New York to the more bucolic setting of the Long Island Forks, I have served with compassion. Since 2011 I have been a Hospice Nurse helping patients of all ages, as well as their families, to achieve comfort and peace.

I'm passionate about the integration of hospice care, Western medicine, with the concepts of Reiki, Compassionate/Therapeutic Touch, Cranio-Sacral Therapy and holistic medicine. I wrote this book with the hope that all medical care providers and volunteers would be open to the use of holistic healing.

Although I first encountered the core concepts of holistic medicine and Reiki in my nursing career, I often find that people consider practical western medicine and holistic practices as two separate islands with very little crossover.

There was some integration in the 70s and the early 80s, but it faded. Only now that we have some scientific evidence of the medical benefits of these practices, are we beginning to see the resurgence of these practices in traditional western medicine. I want to help foster that reintegration.

I wanted to show that western nursing and holistic medicine are *not* two worlds apart. It *is* possible to seamlessly integrate these two practices. I myself have been doing it for forty years. And I think it's the way forward. It is with joy that I see these two schools of thought be reintegrated. But I wanted to lay out a sort of roadmap for a nurse, a doctor, or any medical professional or volunteer trying to integrate these ideas into their day-to-day medical practices and care of not only their patients but also of the families.

I also wanted to demystify and destigmatize the practice of hospice. Hospice care is about bringing grace and comfort to the end of life, and I wanted to use this book to illustrate the journey of one family going through the end-of-life process, to show people what they may expect to encounter if they choose to enter into hospice care.

I would not have been able to write this story without **Patty Alviggi**, my friend of over 40 years, who provided me with a story based on her own family experiences. Through the unexpected loss of her father, she came to understand the need to reach out to other families faced with observing their loved ones go through the process of transitioning from this life into the next. Together, we shared many hardships in our lives. We have stood by and supported one another through it all. I can't begin to thank her enough for connecting the dots of my life and creating this avenue of expression for me. Her selflessness, conscience awareness, and empathetic listening are gifts that make life more soulful for me and for all whose lives are intertwined with hers. We will be forever connected.

Prologue

The Doctor Visit

Jim and his wife Anne held hands and sat in silence. As they waited for the doctor to arrive, Jim felt like he was experiencing *deja vu*. Although it had only been a couple of months, it felt like years had passed since their first visit to this office, when Jim was told that he had a rare, aggressive form of cancer. Jim had a hard time coping with the diagnosis, but in some ways, Anne took the news even harder. "You can't leave me, hon!" She would cry. "I can't even begin to imagine my life without you. We still have so much more to look forward to." Jim and Anne decided that they would do everything they could to fight against his illness. Since then, Jim had spent many, many days in the hospital. The doctors had tried several different treatments, but unfortunately it didn't seem like they were helping. Even worse, all of the treatments and different medicines were making Jim feel nauseous and miserable. He promised Anne and his children that he would never stop fighting, but secretly he feared that this was a losing battle. He didn't want to spend the rest of his days in the hospital, but what other options did he have?

When the doctor entered the room, Jim noticed that his demeanor was more dour than usual. He greeted them with the typical handshake, but not with his usual smile. An immediate sadness enveloped both Jim and Anne, but still they hoped for the best as the doctor sat behind his desk and took a deep breath. "Unfortunately, your latest scan is not looking good," he said frankly, knowing that these were the last words Jim and Anne wanted to hear.

"I do not see any changes for the better, and I am afraid at this point we have exhausted all reasonable measures." Jim was struck silent, but Anne protested. "But aren't there other drugs? New trials? Can't we do *something?*" The doctor shook his head solemnly. "Unfortunately, there's really nothing else for us to try at this time. We could continue chemotherapy, but --"

Anne jumped in. "Okay! Well if chemo's our only option, then let's double it... No, *triple it!*" Even at this somber moment, Jim couldn't help but smile at his wife. Anne was a fighter, and she wouldn't take no for an answer. That was one of the many things he loved about her.

The doctor nodded. "We could continue chemotherapy; however, based on how this has been progressing, I think it's very unlikely that chemo will turn this around."

Anne understood that things were looking hopeless, but she wasn't ready to give up yet. She took Jim's hand and smiled at him tearfully. "Jim and I have been married sixty years, and in that time we've had plenty of little miracles. Is it so crazy to hope for one more?"

"Well," the doctor said. "That's really up to you and Jim. So… Jim? What do you think?"

Jim squeezed his wife's hand and wiped a tear from her cheek. Then he turned to the doctor.

"I keep thinking about the first time we came in here," Jim said. "When you gave me the diagnosis, you told me my life was about to change drastically. You're a real straight shooter doc, and I always liked that about you. So I guess now it's my turn. The truth is, it feels like right now my time is precious, and I've been spending too much of it sitting in this office, talking to you. No offense," he said with a wink. The doctor laughed. Jim continued: "I've been spending too much time in a hospital bed with so many tubes sticking out of me that I look like a set of bagpipes. And when I'm home, I don't get nearly enough quality time with my family, because I'm lying around feeling sick from all this medicine that doesn't seem like it's working. So I'll keep doing the treatment, but I need you to shoot straight with me one more time. Will it be worth it?"

The doctor spoke as decisively as he could. "I don't believe that continuing treatment will cure you or send you into remission. Nor is it going to improve your quality of life. I think you're right; your time right now is precious. It may be time to consider shifting our focus from treatment to comfort and quality of life. And the best treatment I can recommend for *that* is to spend more time at home with your wife and family."

Anne looked stunned. "So that's it? We just *go home?* How am I supposed to manage his pain, or know what to do? You're just gonna leave us on our own?"

"Not at all. Of course, there are some people who choose to spend this time at home without any extra help. But for you and Jim, I would really encourage you to consider hospice care.

Thankfully, I can recommend a great team right in the area." The doctor shuffled through some papers on his desk and handed Jim a pamphlet titled: "WHAT IS HOSPICE CARE?"

"You do have the choice to continue treatment and palliative care if you would prefer. But understand that you will need hospice at *some* point, and I believe that time is now. If you choose hospice, chemotherapy treatment may have to stop, but what you really need now is compassionate care. Because down the road, things are going to get more difficult for both of you. You don't want to be on your own for this stage of life, and I understand that you don't want to be traveling frequently to the hospital for treatments either. So with hospice, you can get all of the necessary help and support that you need. They're available for both medical and holistic needs for you and for your family. I will still be your primary doctor. The medical director and the interdisciplinary team know that they can call our office at any time. They will work with you and our team about your medicine and care. Call the number on the back of this packet when you're ready. The hospice people can meet with you and explain all that they can do for you."

Jim was somewhat overwhelmed by all of this new information, but he agreed to review the materials and consider his options. As Anne and Jim stood to leave, the doctor told them, "Always remember that I am just a phone call away."

The doctor gave Jim a firm handshake. He went to shake Anne's hand as well, but she pulled him into a hug.

When Jim and Anne got home, they sat down together and looked at the packet. Anne shook her head. "I don't get it. You're sick of going to the hospital, but now you want to bring the hospital into our home?" Jim looked at his wife with sad but loving eyes. "Is that what you're worried about?"

"No," Anne shook her head. "That's only part of it. I'm afraid you're giving up. I'm afraid that hospice means the end."

"The doctor didn't say it's the end. He said we may not need it yet, but it's available for us now, *if* we agree to it. It's our decision. So let's just meet with them, learn about the process, and we'll decide then." Anne nodded in agreement, but her heart was still full of doubt.

Chapter One

Meeting the Nurse

Jim and Anne sat in their den, watching the Yankees game on TV. "So," Jim said. "I guess the nurse will be arriving any minute now." Jim turned to Anne, who was passively staring at the screen. "You do remember the agency said they'd be sending her over to talk to us today, don't you?"

After a deep breath, Anne replied "I remember. It's all I've been thinking about."

Anne couldn't help feeling anxious. The idea of bringing a nurse into their home made her uncomfortable. The last time Jim had an extended stay in the hospital, Anne met so many nurses and doctors and PAs and interns that she couldn't keep their names straight. They would come in and wake Jim up at all hours of the night to check his blood pressure and take his temperature, and it seemed like Anne had to constantly remind them what Jim's diagnosis was, what medicines he was taking, what tests they were running... She even had to remind them of Jim's *name*, and she didn't even bother telling them what *her* name was. Anne knew that the nurses were just doing their job, but that was part of the problem. Whenever Anne looked at Jim, lying there in the hospital bed, she saw a loving husband, a war veteran, a proud grandfather, a Yankee fan, and a surprisingly good dancer... But the nurses only saw a name on a medical chart full of bad news. So far, the only thing Anne *liked* about the idea of hospice was that Jim would get to keep his primary care doctor; at least *he* saw Jim as a person, not just a job.

At just that moment, there was a knock on the door. Anne stood up and walked to the foyer. Before she opened the door, she tried to picture the nurse on the other side: Serious face, hospital attire, a stethoscope around her neck and latex gloves on her hands. But when she opened the door, she saw a friendly looking woman in a cute purple sweater standing on the other side.

"Good afternoon," Anne said formally. "You must be the visiting nurse."

"That's me," the nurse said cheerily. "You can call me Lorraine. And *you* must be Anne!"

"Yes, that's right... Why don't you come in?" But before Lorraine could step inside, the house was filled with the sound of a dog barking. Brandy, the family Boxer, wiggled into the foyer, her tail continuously twitching in typical Boxer fashion. She ran right up to Lorraine and started circling her excitedly. Anne was pleasantly surprised; Jim always said that whatever Brandy lacked in manners, she made up for by being a great judge of character.

"Oh, I'm sorry about Brandy," Anne said. "I can put her away." But Lorraine was already bending down to hold Brandy's face and give her a good rubdown. "No, that's okay. I love dogs. I've got two of my own out in the car. See their heads poking out the window? I think they're enjoying this cool weather as much as I am."

Anne took a peek outside, where she saw two friendly looking dogs, grinning in the sunlight. "Aw, they look sweet," Anne said. Brandy followed Lorraine as she stepped inside their home, and Anne closed the front door behind her.

Anne figured that the time for chit-chat was over; the nurse probably wanted to get straight down to business. "So," Anne began. "We still haven't decided if hospice is really the right move for us. I guess we have a lot of questions, but I'm not sure how much time you have…"

"That's okay! No rush," Lorraine assured her. "Today's all about getting to know you and Jim, and letting you get to know about hospice. We can talk about any questions you have. There's no pressure to make any decisions right now."

"Oh," Anne said, pleasantly surprised again. "That's great! Well then, let me introduce you to Jim." Anne started leading Lorraine towards the den, but she stopped when she realized Lorraine was looking at a collection of family photos on the living room wall. "What a great looking bunch!" Lorraine said. "These are all yours?"

"Yes ma'am!" Anne said, beaming. "Jim and I had four of our own, and now we've got three beautiful grandkids. Most of them live close by, so they're always zipping in and out of here. It's been such a relief to have them around, but I told them not to visit today, because we knew that you were coming."

"Oh well, you don't have to send any visitors home on my account!" Lorraine said. "That's one of the best things about hospice care: *You* get to dictate the visiting hours. It's really important that Jim gets to spend as much time as he can at home with the people that he loves. That's what hospice is all about; this is *your* home turf. I'm just here to help."

Anne released a deep breath that she didn't even know she was holding in. She smiled at Lorraine, realizing that her heart was already feeling much lighter. *Maybe this wouldn't be so bad after all.*

"Well," she said, "I guess it's time for you to meet the man of the hour."

* * *

Anne led Lorraine into the den, where Jim was still watching the game on TV, sitting in his favorite armchair with his back to the door. "Jim?" Anne called. "The nurse is here. You think maybe it's time to give the Yankees a rest?"

Jim fumbled for the remote. "Sorry about that. Even when you think that you know how the game's gonna end, it's hard to turn away at the top of the ninth." He muted the television and started to lift himself out of his chair.

"No need to get up!" Lorraine tried to assure him, but Jim was already rising to his feet, using the momentum of a good grunt. "Ah, my legs still work. Better use it or lose it, my dad used to say. He also said you better stand whenever a lady enters the room." He turned to face Lorraine.

"Be careful," Anne winked at Lorraine. "He's a hugger."

"That's great," Lorraine laughed. "I'm a firm believer in hugs. Sometimes a little compassionate touch is the best treatment you can get." Jim smiled at Lorraine. "Well in that case, I could probably use a big one." Lorraine nodded and gave him a good hug.

"I'm Lorraine," she said.

"Pleased to meet you," he replied. "My name's Jim."

"Great name," Lorraine said, smiling. "I've got a son named Jim, except now he spells it J-I-M-I." Jim raised an eyebrow and gave Lorraine a wry grin as if to say *kids these days...*

"Why don't you take a seat," Jim said, gesturing to the couch. "Make yourself comfortable." Lorraine sat down on the couch, while Anne and Jim sat back in their two favorite armchairs. "Have you always been a Yankees fan?" Lorraine asked.

"Yep, my wife and I have been following the Yankees forever. We're both huge fans."

"Jim's a huge fan anyway," Anne confided. "I just like watching #2 if you know what I mean." Lorraine laughed. "I think we all do."

"Oh, it's not just the ladies who love him," said Jim. "I love him too. I mean… Well… you know what I mean." Jim, Lorraine and Anne all laughed together. "Everyone in the family's a Yankees fan," Jim continued. "But there's always one exception. For some reason, my oldest grandson likes the Mets." Lorraine laughed. "A *Mets* fan! How did that happen?" Jim shrugged. "My grandsons used to play ball themselves when they were younger, but that was a while ago. Now I just cheer on my neighbor's son, Ryan. He plays for the county college team. Good kid…"

Anne cut Jim off. "I think that's enough baseball for one day. You know, we *do* have *other* interests."

Jim smirked, pointing to a half-completed jigsaw puzzle on the table. "Ah yes, we've been working hard on our latest jigsaw puzzle too… Well, *I've* been working on the puzzle. *Anne* gave up after finishing the border." Anne laughed and rolled her eyes. Jim whispered to Lorraine. "I like to let her do the easy part."

Lorraine chuckled. Her eyes wandered from the jigsaw puzzle on the coffee table as she took in the room around her, gathering up little details about Jim and Anne's life together. The den seemed like it was Jim's sanctuary. There were more family photos on the wall, a bookshelf brimming with history books, a small collection of model planes on a windowsill…

"Ah, so you noticed my model planes," said Jim. "See the one on the left there? That's a B-47 Stratojet. I flew one of those towards the end of the Korean War."

"Really?" Lorraine asked. "Wow, thank you for serving our country. You were in the Air Force?"

"*Captain* of the Air Force." Jim said proudly. "I was a part of the Devil's Own Bomb Squadron. Thankfully though, the war was nearly over just as I signed up, so I didn't see much action. I guess I got lucky back then," he said, absentmindedly playing with a medal that hung around his neck. Lorraine had recognized it right away.

"That's a Saint Christopher's medal you're wearing, isn't it?" Lorraine asked. "Someone must have been looking out for you." Jim noticed that he had been fiddling with it and nodded. "That's right," he said. "The patron saint who protects travelers. Anne gave me that medal just before I went off to bootcamp."

"That's beautiful... Do you mind if I ask then, are you and Anne religious at all?"

Jim shrugged. "I was raised Protestant, but I haven't been to my church since I retired from the Air Force. Anne's a Catholic. And that's how we raised the kids."

Lorraine nodded. "I know that's kind of a personal question, but it can be good for us to know. For instance, I can always contact a local pastor for you, if you want their support."

"No, I don't think so... Well, Anne and I can talk it over, and we'll figure it all out. Thank you though," Jim said. Jim and Anne smiled at each other a little nervously, as if for a moment they had all forgotten the real reason for Lorraine's visit. For a while the room had been filled with the banter of new friends; but now there was a subtle shift in the conversation. Suddenly the subject of hospice, and the seriousness of the nurse's visit, seeped into their cozy den like the smell of old cigar smoke. Lorraine recognized the sudden pall cast over the room, and she made a point to transition to the subject of hospice as gently as possible. "It really is wonderful to meet both of you," she said. "And I'm sorry that we have to meet like this."

Anne nodded. "It's certainly not what we expected. Jim just retired."

"Retired! What kind of work do you do?" Lorraine asked him.

"I'm a CPA."

"Well, good for you. I'm sure it was a *taxing* job." Lorraine said, grinning. Jim stared blankly for a moment and then laughed. "Ah - Yes, haha, I get it. Very taxing indeed."

* * *

The Yankees game was finally over (they lost, just as Jim had predicted), so he switched off the television and turned his full attention towards Lorraine.

"So," he began somewhat uneasily, "how does this... work exactly?"

"Well, this is really an informational visit," Lorraine explained. "I know that choosing whether or not hospice is right for you can be a lot to process. So today, I'm here to sit with you and Anne, tell you a little about what hospice is really about, and hopefully I can answer any questions you might have. To start with, how did you hear about us?"

Jim answered. "Well, lately it's become clear that my treatment isn't working as well as we'd like, so my doctor gave us an information packet about hospice. He's the one who recommended that we call you, and I've always trusted him. So we read through the literature that he provided, but I have to say I'm still not sure I understand it all. I guess I always thought hospice means you have to go to the hospital, and that you'll probably die any minute, or at least within a couple of weeks... Now, I'll admit, these days I'm not exactly in ship-shape, but frankly I was a little surprised that my doctor thought we were already at that stage."

"I hear what you're saying," Lorraine replied. "I think all too often people only turn to hospice at the very end, so when most people think about hospice, they think it always signifies a matter of days or weeks, when in fact it's available much earlier than that."

Anne cleared her throat nervously. "From what I read, they don't really offer hospice to patients if they think they have more than six months to go... So, even if it's more than a couple *weeks*, it's still a lot less time than we'd like to have."

Lorraine nodded sympathetically. "Of course. Although we do have patients who are with us for longer than six months, that is generally the recommended time-frame. Either way, I can only imagine how hard it must be to process all this. And let me just say, I'm not here to push you to make any decisions you're not ready to make yet. But I will say that sometimes it can be a blessing to start at-home hospice care *before* it's an absolute necessity. While you still have some health and energy, you can use this time to be at home, enjoy the company of your family, and one another. You won't be spending all that time in a hospital, and yet you'll still have plenty of medical and emotional support from the hospice team."

Jim and Anne thought about that silently for a moment, looking at each other nearly the whole time. After a minute, Jim turned back to Lorraine and said, "If we *did* choose to start hospice, what does the process... look like? I mean what kind of "support" do you offer?"

Lorraine began to walk them through it. "Well, once we get you signed up, we'll make sure you've got whatever you need to be safe and comfortable at home. We also give you what we call a 'comfort kit,' so you have all the medicine you may need without having to go to the pharmacy. Of course, you don't have to take any medication, but it's right there for you in the fridge if you need it.

"Then there's your support team. You'll have a primary nurse, that will be me. You'll also have an LPN -- a Licensed Practical Nurse. Generally, a nurse will be visiting once a week. During a typical visit, they'll come over, check your blood pressure and your heart rate, make sure you're not experiencing too much pain or discomfort. They're there to manage your medicine and your pain, teach you how to use the medication properly, and help with any other medical needs you may have.

"We also offer nursing as needed, so if you need someone to come by outside of those weekly visits, even in the middle of the night, somebody from our team is always just a phone call away. So any time you're having pain or any sort of emergency, you don't have to decide between going to the hospital or handling it on your own. Just give us a call, and we can talk you through it then and there to answer any questions or concerns you may have, or we can come to you at any time if you could use a hand."

Jim seemed relieved. "That's actually really good to hear. There have been a few times where I've felt very sick or like I was in a lot of pain, and we couldn't decide whether we should just try to let it pass, or if we should call an ambulance. Sometimes it felt like neither option was very good."

Lorraine nodded. "I completely understand, and that's exactly what we're here for. In addition to nursing, we have an entire support team where you need it. The other principal person who will be working with you is a social worker, who can give you all kinds of support. They're here to help you, Jim, with all your non-medical needs, but they're also here for Anne and the rest of your family. During a time like this, there can be a lot to keep track of, and a social worker can help you with a lot of those big decisions, not to mention emotional support. We've also got volunteers and home health aids, people that can help you make a bed or take a bath, or just hang at home with you if Anne needs to run some errands. Really, you've got a whole wonderful team of people to help you when you need it most."

Jim nodded, looking pretty impressed. At first, Anne seemed to be taking it all fairly positively herself, but now she was starting to look upset again. Lorraine turned to her. "Anne," Lorraine asked. "Do *you* have any questions or concerns?"

Anne shook her head. "My only real concern is that we're giving up too early," said Anne. She looked down at her lap, unable to meet either of their eyes.

Jim sighed and smiled softly at Lorraine. Taking Anne's hand, he explained, "It's like I said when you walked in at the end of the Yankees game: Even if you know how the game's gonna end, it's always hard to turn away at the top of the ninth." Anne and Lorraine both smiled at that.

"Okay," Anne cleared her throat. "Here's a hypothetical question. If something happens… Maybe a new drug trial opens up that Jim could qualify for… or even if we decide to go back on chemo… can we still do that after we choose hospice? Or is that simply no longer an option?"

"That's something we can always discuss if and when the time comes. But it's not unusual for a patient to be discharged so that they can try some new form of treatment. And nothing would make us happier than if you found something that worked for you. Our hospice consent form is not a binding agreement. You have a say in every aspect of this process, and you can end our contract at any time. *And* if you choose to come back, you can always start hospice with us again."

Anne breathed a sigh of relief. "Okay," she said, "that is good to know."

Lorraine nodded. "In the meantime, just know that we are here to help you and your family in any way that we can. Our goal is to make you as comfortable as possible for as long as you are in our care."

* * *

Lorraine answered some more of their questions and put Anne and Jim's minds at ease about a few other matters. After she left the house, Jim went upstairs to take a nap. A little while later, Anne went upstairs and laid down beside him in bed. Jim opened his eyes and looked at her.

"So," Anne said, "what did you think?"

"I liked her," Jim said. "She was nice. Kind and honest. She answered our questions, heard our concerns, and she seemed to have a lot of compassion… If I'm being honest, she really made me feel like this is the right decision for us."

After a long pause, Anne sighed and nodded her head. "As long as you're comfortable with it," she said. "It is good to know we can revoke hospice care if we find another treatment option. In the meantime, it seems like she really does care about respecting our wishes."

Jim nodded. They looked at each other for a long time then. They both had so much on their minds, and they wanted nothing more than to give each other words of comfort and confidence, but in this moment, it seemed as if they had nothing else to say. Perhaps they had made up their minds about hospice after all.

Without saying another word, Jim and Anne closed their eyes and fell asleep in each other's arms, as they had done almost every night for the last sixty years of their lives.

Chapter Two

The Social Worker

Later that evening, Jim called the hospice center to say that he would like to begin service. Thankfully, they told him that they could start hospice right away, and they could return as early as the next day. This time, Lorraine would be joined by Shanice, a social worker, and together they would help Jim with what they called an "admission," officially signing him into hospice care. Jim set up a time for the following afternoon, and went to bed feeling relieved and also a little nervous.

* * *

The next morning over breakfast, Anne and Jim heard the doorbell ring. They looked at each other, surprised. "That couldn't be them, could it? They're a little early..." Anne got up to answer the door while Jim sat at the breakfast table, his brow furrowed. Suddenly, he heard the house fill with voices, all of them chattering in the foyer. Jim couldn't hear them very well, since Brandy the Boxer was barking her head off, but he thought he could make out the voice of his daughter, Patty.

"Patty? Is that you?" He called out into the foyer.

"Hi, Dad!" Patty shouted back. "Yes, it's me. I thought I'd pop over for a visit!"

"Not just Patty! I'm here too!" called another voice. This was his oldest daughter, Kylee.

"And Jimmy!" called out one of his sons.

"And Peter!" shouted his youngest.

His four children piled into the kitchen all at once. Jim supposed they weren't children anymore, although he'd probably always think of them that way. In fact, by now Patty had two adult sons of her own: Bobby, who lived in Myrtle Beach, and Brian, who lives with his wife Amanda. Even Jim's youngest son Peter was a father now. He and his wife Angela had a daughter named Mikayla. At six years old, she was Jim's youngest grandchild, a real sweetheart too.

Seeing his four children all crowding together in their kitchen filled Jim's heart with joy, although he didn't know if this was the best time for an impromptu visit.

"What are you kids doing here?" he asked, smiling.

"We just wanted to see how you're doing," said Patty.

"Mom told us you're starting hospice," Kylee said, getting right down to business.

"News travels fast, huh?" Jim said, smirking at his wife, who was standing in the kitchen doorway. She looked at Jim innocently, like she was just as surprised as he was that the kids had found out.

"I wish we knew you were all coming," Jim said. "I'm not sure if today's really the best time. The hospice people should be here any minute."

"We know," said Peter. "That's why we're here. We might have some questions of our own. Make sure you know what you're signing."

"We're just here to support you, Dad," said Jimmy.

Jim turned to Anne. She smiled. "What? The nurse said *we* dictate the visiting hours here. So, what's so wrong with having a couple visitors?"

At just that moment, the doorbell rang. Brandy started barking and wagging her tail, getting excited all over again.

"Well," Jim said, "I guess the more the merrier."

* * *

As Lorraine was welcomed into the house, Jim saw that she had brought someone else with her: the social worker, Shanice. Jim was worried that meeting the whole family at once would be overwhelming for the hospice workers, but Lorraine and Shanice seemed completely undaunted by all the visitors as they cheerfully introduced themselves to everyone. Jim noticed that having the whole family there seemed to be making Anne more comfortable as well. With a house full of company, Anne was totally in her element. She chatted up her kids to Lorraine and Shanice, excitedly boasting about each of their various accomplishments while simultaneously pouring coffee and juice for everyone. After a few minutes of idle chit chat, everyone had a seat at the kitchen table.

"So I think I already said hi to everyone," said Shanice, "but just in case, my name's Shanice. It's really nice to meet you all, and it's lovely to see that Jim's got such a great team behind him at home." Lorraine spoke up. "Shanice is an excellent social worker. She's extremely knowledgeable and has a ton of experience. You're in very good hands with her."

"A social worker?" Asked Jimmy, a bit confused. "Why do we need a social worker?"

"Well," Shanice explained, "I'm mainly here as an advocate for Jim, and also for you - the family. It's my job to support you through this whole process. This can be a stressful time; I'm here to make sure you have the information and the resources you need to get through it, whether that's emotional, familial, financial, spiritual… Basically, whatever we can do to make sure this time is easier for you, we will try our best. We want to make sure that Jim has everything he needs during this stage, *and* we want to make sure that everyone is prepared for the next stage as well…"

Jim and Anne saw their kids exchanging looks when Shanice mentioned this; none of them were ready to think about the *next* stage yet, about what came *after*. But just hearing that Shanice would be there to guide them through all of those difficult decisions brought them some comfort already.

* * *

Shanice placed a short packet of forms on the kitchen table. "Now we can get your admission and consent paperwork completed. The doctor sent me your medical background, so all I need is your signature on the consent forms, and then I can begin your medical assessment."

Lorraine and Shanice went through and explained each page as thoroughly as they could before Jim signed each document. Occasionally Jim would pause and he or his family members would read something over more closely, but they moved through most of the forms fairly quickly.

There was only one document left to sign. Before presenting it to him, Shanice said "this is a DNR / DNI form." She stressed that he did not have to sign it, and that him and his family would have time to discuss whether or not this was the right decision for him. He was not under any obligation to sign the form right away, and he would retain the right to rip up the form and end service at any time.

Peter spoke up. "I've heard of a DNR, but what does it mean exactly?"

"Well," Shanice explained, "These orders are legal instructions written by Jim's doctor to be signed by Jim. Their sole purpose is to inform his family and healthcare team of Jim's wishes in the event of any life-threatening health emergency." Shanice turned and spoke to Jim directly. "If you choose to sign a 'Do Not Resuscitate order,'" Shanice continued, "it means that if you were to have a life-threatening health emergency, you would not want anyone to take extraordinary measures to save your life, such as performing CPR or defibrillation. On the other hand, A 'Do Not Intubate' order, or 'DNI' would *allow* certain life-saving measures like CPR, but it would dictate that you do *not* want a breathing tube, or to be put on any form of life support... Of course, in any event, we would still continue all measures that would provide comfort, such as pain management, antibiotics, stopping any bleeding, et cetera..."

The silence in the room spoke volumes. Jim hesitated, shaking his head. "To be honest, a DNR is... not something I ever really thought about. Anne and I haven't even written a living will..." Jim turned to Anne, and for a moment he seemed a little lost and helpless. But Anne looked back at him with confidence: *Don't worry*, the look said. *We're going to figure all this out.* Jim turned back to Shanice. "I think I need to discuss this with my wife before signing anything," he said.

"Of course," said Shanice, nodding assuredly. "I know that this is a lot to take in. It's a really difficult decision that you may not be ready to make yet. And that decision may *change* over time too, based on where you see yourself and your overall health as we move forward. So just think about it, talk it over, and don't hesitate to ask me or the team any questions, now or at any time in the future. We're here to help explain anything we can. You also may want to reach out to your doctor for additional clarification and support while you're contemplating your options. Just remember, this is a choice that only you and your family can make. All medical personnel must abide by your wishes."

Jim nodded. Shanice waited to see if Jim or the family had any more questions, but it seemed like they had more than enough information to digest for the moment. Jim skipped past the DNR/DNI page, signed the last couple of forms, and put down his pen with a sigh.

Lorraine smiled. "Whew, and that's the last one! I know that took a while, but I promise it won't be like that for our future visits. Thankfully all of that paperwork is behind us now."

Jim grinned at Lorraine. "I'm a CPA, remember? I could fill out forms in my sleep."

* * *

After Anne treated everyone to a second cup of coffee, Shanice put the paperwork away.

"Just a couple quick things before we get out of your hair for today. First, I wanted to let you know that tomorrow or the next day, you'll be receiving what is commonly referred to as a 'comfort kit.'

"It's standard practice for our medical director to order this for every new hospice patient, so we'll have it shipped out to you within the next few days.

"The comfort kit is somewhere between a pocket-pharmacy and a well-stocked medicine cabinet," Lorraine said with a bit of a chuckle. "We recommend that you put it in the refrigerator where everyone will know where to find it. Basically the idea behind giving hospice patients this box is so that you will have immediate access to necessary medications, rather than having to go through the process of getting a prescription from your doctor or a nurse practitioner, and then needing to fill it at the pharmacy. The comfort kit makes all that much simpler. It should have all the medicines you may need. And whether or not you choose to take them, because it *is* your choice, we are always available to help you understand how to use the medicine, and how to make sure Jim's getting the dose he's comfortable with."

"What kind of medicine?" Jim asked, his eyebrow slightly raised. Jim was always a bit stubborn about pain medicine, the kind of guy who would walk around with sore joints or a busted knee for days before he ever caved and took an Advil.

"Inside the comfort kit you'll have Morphine for pain and shortness of breath, Lorazepam and Haloperidol for anxiety or agitation, Acetaminophen for fever, Compazine for nausea, Dulcolax for constipation, and a couple medications that help if you have difficulty swallowing. But you'll decide with your doctor what medicines are best for you, and they'll be there if you need them. When the kit arrives, Shanice and I or another nurse will walk you through it to explain each of the medications in greater detail, but I'm glad I got to explain it while the whole family is here."

Jim nodded gruffly. "I might skip it if that's okay. I don't want to get all loopy on a bunch of pain meds."

"Again, we'll completely respect your wishes in regards to that. But while you may be experiencing minimal pain right now, that can change at any time, and it can do so without warning. So we just want you to be prepared in case you discover that you do need some medicine after all."

"We'll also be sending over some other medical equipment for you too," added Shanice. "You'll be getting an over-the-bed tray table, a bedside commode, a transport wheelchair, and oxygen. The oxygen and the commode are just for convenience and is to be used only if needed. Also if you'd like, we can also order you a reclining chair and a hospital bed."

"Oh," Anne sounded worried. "You don't think he needs a *hospital bed*, does he? Where would we even put it?"

Jim let out a deep sigh. "No, I don't need a hospital bed. I'm *fine*." The kids smiled secretly at each other across the table. "I'm *fine*" was one of their dad's classic refrains.

"If you want to keep sleeping in your own bed, by all means, you should," Lorraine said. "But we can always address that again later if necessary."

Shanice chimed in. "We just want to make sure you have everything you may need right here at home, and to make sure the house is safe and well-equipped if and when you experience any decline in mobility. Speaking of which, unless you have any questions right now, I'd like to take a quick walkthrough of the house, just to look out for any potential safety concerns."

Anne got to her feet, always eager to give a tour. "I'll show you around if you'd like."

"That would be lovely," said Shanice, and the two of them exited the kitchen. As they walked through the rooms, Shanice took notes on things like fire extinguishers and smoke detectors and whether they had any firearms in the house. She checked the rugs, the steps, the height of the toilet, the step up into the shower, the balance bar installed in the shower, and everything else that could become important as Jim's mobility declined.

* * *

Meanwhile in the kitchen, Lorraine was sitting with Jim and his kids. "The last thing I would like to do before wrapping up for the day is to check your vitals, meaning take your blood pressure, listen to your heart rate, and check your lungs. Is that okay?" Jim nodded, and Lorraine continued. "First, is there anything that is causing you pain right now?"

Jim smiled. "If I say yes, are you going to dope me up?" Lorraine laughed and shook her head no. "Well," Jim continued, "thankfully all of my hospital visits have taught me how to put this. I'm about a 5 out of 10 in my right shoulder right now."

"Only shoulder pain? That's good. If you'd like, I can check with your doctor about getting you a prescription for pain medication, if you don't already have one," said Lorraine.

"No, really, it's tolerable. I'll just do what I always do and use the heating pad." Jim rotated his shoulder to show how flexible he still was, but even that made him wince in pain. He groaned. "You sure you don't want any medicine, Dad?" asked Patty, but Jim shook his head.

"If you don't mind," Lorraine offered, "I'd like to try something that may help minimize your shoulder pain. No medicine, no heating pad." Jim raised an eyebrow. "You're not gonna try to crack my back are you?" Lorraine laughed. "No, no," she said, chuckling, "nothing like that. It's just my version of a Light Touch Massage, or what some people call Therapeutic Touch or Healing Touch. It might help reduce the pain a bit." After a moment, Jim shrugged. "Why not? I guess it can't hurt," he replied.

After checking Jim's vitals, Lorraine placed her hands slightly above Jim's shoulders and held them there for a short while. Jim wasn't sure what she was doing at first. She wasn't really massaging his shoulder. In fact, she wasn't even touching him… Then all at once he felt an unexpected heat radiating to his shoulder, and a sense of calm came over his face. Lorraine then followed with a short and gentle massage.

Jim looked up at her, surprised. "Wow, that *does* feel better. What did you do?" Lorraine smiled. "It's Therapeutic Touch, something I learned from studying holistic medicine. It's something you can do that can reduce pain and alleviate some stress."

Jim nodded his thanks, but his daughter Patty seemed more interested. "I've heard something about that," she said. "Maybe you can explain it to me sometime." Lorraine nodded excitedly. "Sure, I'd love to!"

Just then, Shanice returned from her tour of the house with Anne. Lorraine and Shanice exchanged a quick look; it had been a long day for Jim and everyone, and they didn't want to overstay their welcome. They said their goodbyes and headed for the door. Jimmy, the oldest son, walked them to the door. On their way out, he shook their hands, and thanked them both sincerely.

"When my mom called me to say that my dad was starting hospice, I have to admit, she didn't sound like she liked the idea very much... I'm not sure how much I liked it either. But today, after meeting you both, I think we all feel a bit better. All of this would have been too much for my mom to handle on her own. It's really good to know that even when me or my brother or sisters can't be here, we've got you on our side. So, thanks. It means a lot."

Shanice smiled. "You've got a wonderful family. It's good to know we've got *you* on *our* side. We'll see you soon. Be well." And with that, Lorraine and Shanice left.

Chapter Three

The Fall

A few weeks had passed since Jim's admission into hospice, and Anne was feeling cautiously optimistic; so far, nothing had really changed about their lives. Their daily routines were still perfectly intact. Their house had not suddenly transformed (as Anne had initially feared) into a hospital, bustling with nurses and ominous medical equipment. Of course the hospice organization had called to check in a couple of times, but their conversations were short and pleasant, not nearly as daunting or time-consuming as their admission visit. Best of all, Jim seemed in good spirits, and it felt like the shadow hanging over their home had begun to pass, at least for now. But then this morning, something unusual and surprising finally *did* happen: Anne woke up before Jim.

Jim had always risen at the crack of dawn, a habit drilled into him from his days in the Air Force. Anne could count the number of times she'd made the first pot of coffee on one hand; that was always Jim's job. But this morning, the sun was rising in the east, the birds were singing, and Jim was still snoring soundly, sleeping like a rock. Anne was happy to see it; the last couple of nights Jim had been tossing and turning quite a bit. Anne knew it would do him good to let him sleep in a while longer, so she climbed out of bed and quietly left the room, closing the door behind her.

She shuffled into the kitchen, deciding that she'd make a full pot of coffee after all. She hoped Jim would keep sleeping, but she knew that no matter how deep his slumber was, the smell of fresh coffee in the percolator would beckon him from his sleep and he'd make a beeline straight from bed to his favorite mug in the kitchen cabinet. Anne was midway through counting out tablespoons of coffee when she heard a crash.

"Hon?" She called out, but there was no response. She tried telling herself that she'd imagined the noise. Maybe it was just the dog; it wouldn't be the first time Brandy had gone sniffing around in the closet and wound up with a hamper full of dirty laundry on her head. But Anne didn't like the sound, or the silence that now resonated from the bedroom. She called his name tepidly as she left the kitchen. She heard a groan as she came around the corner, and saw Jim lying on the floor, halfway out of their room, curled around the doorway in the fetal position. She rushed over to his side. "Jim? What happened?" she asked, trying to keep the panic out of her voice. Jim groaned again. He sounded more frustrated than pained, and that was a good sign. But he was still lying on his side, and he wasn't trying to get to his feet, at least not yet.

"I went to open the door and… I don't know." He mumbled. "Must have just tripped or… Stupid…" His voice trailed off, and he tried to clear his throat.

"Is anything broken? Are you hurt?" She asked. "No," he sighed. "No. My shoulder hurts a little, but I'm okay. I'm okay. Just help me up." He looked up at her, and that's when she saw the cut above his right eye. There was a little blood trickling along one bushy eyebrow, but thankfully the cut was small, and the blood wasn't getting in his eye. "Oh, honey, you're bleeding," she said. "I don't know if you should get up."

"Ridiculous," he grumbled. "I'm fine." He reached out a hand for the doorframe, trying to pull himself to his feet, but he moaned again and dropped his arm to the floor. Anne wanted to help him, but she thought better of it. "I'm calling the nurse. I don't want you getting up. Just stay right there." He responded with an annoyed grunt, and Anne rushed back to the kitchen to call the hospice center. As she dialed them, Jim called out from the hallway. "Don't bother them, Anne. It's nothing." But Anne persisted; Lorraine had told her several times she could call any time, day or night. They picked up after the first ring.

"Hospice center, this is David speaking. How can I help you?"

"My husband fell," Anne blurted out, caught off guard by the tremble in her own voice. "I -- I'm home alone and I'm not sure what to do."

"That's okay, we're here," Nurse David said calmly, and Anne found herself taking a deep breath. He asked for Jim's full name, birthday, and their address so he could send someone over if necessary. "Is he alert? In pain? Any bleeding?" David asked, still maintaining that calm in his voice.

Anne tried to mirror David's tone, but her words rushed out in an anxious flood. "Yes, he's alert. He does have a cut. There's not much blood but the cut's on his head... And he said his shoulder hurts. Only a little, but that could just be his old tough guy routine; he'd probably tell me the same thing if his arm fell right off. I don't know… He says he's fine, but he's still lying there on the floor… Maybe I'm just overreacting…"

"Not at all, you did the right thing in calling us. I see that Lorraine is on the schedule. I'll give her a call. In the meantime, bring Jim a pillow or some cushions, maybe a chair if you have one handy. If he's able to pull himself up, you can hold him and guide him into a chair. But don't force him or pull him up yourself if he can't really move. Better to leave him lying down."

"Okay," Anne nodded fervently. She could hear Jim groaning in the hallway.

Nurse David continued. "Okay, let me reach out to Lorraine and see if she's in the area. Either way, we'll get a nurse over there soon…"

"Anne," Jim called from the hallway. "I'm getting up."

"I think he's trying to stand," Anne said into the phone. "I have to go."

"Okay," David said. "Just sit tight and take a deep breath. Someone will be there soon."

Anne hung up the phone. Rushing back into the hallway, she saw that Jim had managed to stand. He was leaning against the doorframe, still wobbling on his feet. "Are you okay?" Anne asked.

He nodded. "Just a little dizzy I guess." Anne went to grab him a chair. By the time she got Jim sitting down and had cleaned the blood off his forehead (the cut wasn't that bad after all), Anne's heart had finally stopped racing. Once the color returned to Jim's face, he looked over at the kitchen. "Did I hear you making coffee?" he asked. "I could really go for a cup right now." And even though Anne had been seized with terror only five minutes ago, now she found herself laughing until she had tears streaming down her cheeks.

* * *

Twenty minutes later, the doorbell rang. Anne was more than relieved to see Lorraine standing on the doorstep. Once she had examined Jim, Lorraine told him that it didn't look like he'd broken anything. "But if you would prefer, we always have the option to call the ambulance so they can take a look at the hospital."

Jim waved it off. "No, no. Anne worries too much. I wouldn't have even called if it was up to me. All I need is a band-aid for the cut, and maybe you could talk me into taking a Tylenol."

Lorraine nodded. "If that's what you'd like. I just want to make sure you're feeling okay."

Jim nodded, then he thought about something for a second. "Well maybe…" he began, then trailed off.

"What is it, hon?" Anne asked.

Jim turned to Lorraine. "What was that thing you did to my shoulder the other day? Light Touch or whatever it was? That wasn't too bad, ya know."

Anne rolled her eyes, grinning. "He's underselling it," she said. "He told *me* that his shoulder hadn't felt that good in years. Said you were a miracle worker."

Lorraine laughed. "Oh, I'm no miracle worker. It's just a form of holistic healing I studied. It goes by many different names, because they have different versions of it all over the world. Some call it Therapeutic Touch, Healing Touch, Compassionate Touch, Light Massage... Many people know it as Reiki, where there's no actual *physical* contact between the patient and the practitioner. There are different approaches to all of them, but they have many similarities."

Jim nodded, impressed, but still reserving any comments.

"Thank God you're here," Anne sighed, and Lorraine saw that Anne had a tear in the corner of her eye. "When he had his fall this morning, I... It just felt like the hospital all over again. It's like no matter how badly I want to help, I don't actually *know* anything. I feel like I don't have any control over any of this, like there's nothing I can do to help when he's in pain..." A tear spilled down her cheek. "Sorry. I'm just glad you're here. That's all I meant to say."

"I can show you if you like," Lorraine said, smiling.

"Show me what?" Anne asked, still sniffling. "The Ray Key thing?"

Lorraine nodded, stifling a small giggle. "Of course! Reiki's easy to learn. The basics anyway. It's something you can do for him even when he's not in pain. It could be helpful for both of you."

Anne smiled, wiping away her tears. "Really? You'd show me?"

"I would love to," Lorraine said, putting her arm around Anne's shoulder. "You can watch me do it for a minute. Then I'll let you take over."

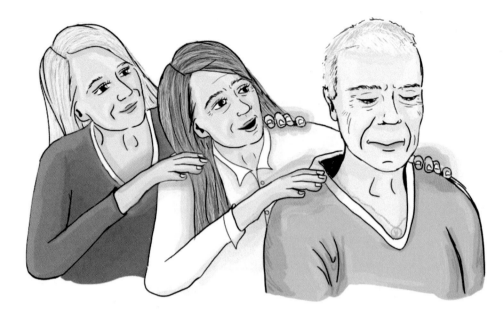

After a short demonstration, Lorraine showed Anne how to hold her hands over Jim's shoulders. Then Lorraine stood behind Anne, and held her hands over Anne's shoulders in the same way. "You can do what I do," Lorraine said.

Anne followed Lorraine's instructions. After a moment, she looked back at Lorraine, her eyes lighting up. "Wow," she said, "I feel a lot of heat."

Lorraine smiled. "That's right, you're drawing the pain out of his shoulder."

Anne nodded. "I can feel what you're doing too. All that tension is leaving my neck."

"You see?" Jim asked, his eyes closed, smiling peacefully. "Miracle worker. Just like I said."

***

A little while later, Anne walked Lorraine to the door.

"Thank you," Anne said sincerely. "You know, I've been so focused on Jim's needs, I didn't realize that *I* could use some Compassionate Touch *myself.* Not to mention, teaching me how to do that for Jim…" She shook her head. "All of this has been really scary for me. And the worst part is that helpless feeling, like I have no control, like there's nothing I can do. And sure, I could always bring him to the hospital, I could always make a phone call, but this was different. This felt like I was really helping him." They reached the front door.

"Jim is so lucky to have you, you know" Lorraine said. "I've only known you for a couple of weeks, but I don't think you could be helpless if you tried. Even when you're scared, you always seem like you're in control. And that energy you have? *That's* what's keeping Jim alive. Compassionate Touch is just one way of harnessing that power, sharing that positive, healing energy. But you've always had it inside you."

Anne wanted to tell Lorraine that she was an angel, but for the moment, she was speechless. So instead, she pulled Lorraine into a hug.

Chapter Four
A Gradual Change In Routine

It was a little after ten in the morning when Peter, Anne and Jim's youngest son, pulled his car up to his parents' home. A gleeful shout came from the backseat. "Yay! Grandma and Grandpa's house!" Peter looked in the rearview mirror and winked at his daughter, Mikayla, who was excitedly unbuckling her seatbelt. Mikayla loved her grandparents, and Peter knew that they couldn't get enough of her either. Peter cherished the close-knit relationship between his parents and his daughter, but a part of him was worried that soon he would have to explain to her that Grandpa was dying, and what that meant exactly. At six years old, Mikayla might have had some familiarity with the concept of death, but it hadn't really hit home for her yet. She'd never experienced the death of a loved one, not even a beloved pet. Peter knew that soon the day would come where he would have to have a difficult conversation with her. But for now, the most important thing was letting Mikayla spend as much time with her Grandpa as possible. Peter followed his daughter with a smile as she skipped up to the house and rang the doorbell. Anne answered the door, her eyes lighting up. She said hello and gave them both a big hug and a kiss.

"Where's Grandpa?" Mikayla asked.

"You just missed him! He's taking Brandy on her morning walk, but he'll be back soon."

Peter smiled at his mom. "So, Dad's still doing his morning walk, huh? That's good! He must be feeling okay, then."

"Yeah, I think so." Anne shrugged. "I'm always a little reluctant to let him go on his own, but you know Dad. It's his routine. He wants to go for a walk? I won't stand in his way." She laughed.

Just then, the front door flung open. It was Ryan, their next-door neighbor. He was gripping Brandy's leash with one hand. He had his other arm around Jim's shoulder. Jim was hobbling on one leg, and he looked a little pale. "What happened?" Anne asked, alarmed.

"I'm fine," Jim grumbled. "I just tripped over the dog leash." Jim seemed alert, and like he was suffering more embarrassment than pain at the moment.

Ryan explained, sounding a little out of breath. "I looked out my window and saw Mr. A lying on the ground in front of my house. He seemed okay by the time I got to him. But still, I thought I should help him back home."

"Thanks for throwing me under the bus, Ryan," Jim joked. "Only kidding. I can't thank you enough."

Ryan and Peter eased Jim into a chair. Despite how calm Jim was acting, Anne started panicking when she noticed the blood soaking through one leg of his pants. Peter offered to call 911, but Anne told him that he didn't need to. She was already dialing Lorraine. When it came to Jim's care, the family had complete trust in Lorraine and the hospice nurses. She would know what to do.

Lorraine reassured Anne that she had made the right call. There was no need for anyone to call 911, since Jim was alert, oriented and able to walk on his own. Lorraine said that she was with a patient right now, but she would come over as soon as she'd finished up.

* * *

Lorraine arrived at the house about thirty minutes later. She saw Peter and little Mikayla playing on the front lawn with Brandy, the family dog. She gave them a friendly wave, and they waved back. Now that the family had adapted to Lorraine and Shanice's frequent visits, everyone felt much more comfortable having them around. Lorraine and Shanice had begun to feel like part of the extended family, dropping by just like any other relatives, never knowing who would be home when they got there.

Lorraine turned around to the backseat, where her dog Lance was sticking his head out of the open window. "I'll be right back, Lance!" she said. Lance yawned his approval, and Lorraine stepped out of the car.

"Hey, Mikayla!" She called. "Hey, Peter. How's everybody doing?"

"Grandpa fell down," Mikayla said matter-of-factly. "He tripped over Brandy's leash, so now *we're* taking her for a walk. Did you bring your dogs again?" She asked, excitedly.

Lorraine nodded. "Lance is in the back seat, if you and Brandy wanna say hi!" Mikayla and Brandy ran over to her car. Lance gave them both a happy grin from the back seat.

Peter smiled at Lorraine. "I figured we'd take the dog out and give you some space in there."

Lorraine shrugged. "Oh well, don't mind me. Is Jim alright, though?"

"Yeah, I think he's fine," Peter said. He lowered his voice a little, adding, "I just don't want Mikayla to get upset if she hears too much of the… *grown-up* talk."

Lorraine nodded. "It can be hard talking to kids about this stuff. It can be hard with *adults* too. One of my dogs passed away this week, and I still haven't talked about it with anyone."

Peter patted Lorraine's shoulder. "Ah, I'm sorry to hear that," he said.

Lorraine nodded her thanks and smiled over at Mikayla, playing with the two dogs. "But you know, children can be surprisingly resilient. I find that very often they seem to know more than we give them credit for." They looked back over at Mikayla, who was giving Lance a kiss through the window. Peter and Lorraine both sighed.

* * *

"What were you doing when you fell?" Lorraine asked Jim while she cleaned and bandaged the cut on his swollen knee.

"Fall? I didn't *fall.* I was just picking weeds." Jim said innocently, trying for a little levity.

Lorraine smirked. "Your granddaughter said you tripped over the dog leash."

Jim laughed. "Alright, Lorraine. You got me."

Lorraine smiled. "I've been doing this long enough to know when someone's giving me the old run-around. *Everybody* falls. But it's always the big brave military men who hate admitting it."

Jim chuckled as she finished bandaging his cut. She looked up at him more seriously then, and added "You have to know that falling is nothing to be ashamed of. It's part of the process. It's a sign that the body is weakening." Jim grumbled quietly. Lorraine put an ice pack on his swollen knee and asked if he was in any pain, but Jim told her his leg felt fine now.

"Now how about your shoulder?" she asked.

"Pain's about a five out of ten," Jim shrugged. Yet it was evident to everyone that he was doing worse than he was willing to admit; when Lorraine raised his arm ever so slightly, he winced in pain. "I feel fine," he repeated, feeling frustrated. "And I'm not going to the hospital!"

"We don't have to go to the hospital," Lorraine said. "But I think you'd feel better if you let me give you some pain meds and a little Therapeutic Touch." Jim agreed to the massage, but turned down the medicine for now. So Lorraine laid her hands over his knee. While she gave him a Light Touch Massage, he closed his eyes and breathed deeply. Then she massaged his shoulders. When she was finished, he looked at her calmly.

"Thank you," he said. "That felt great. To tell you the truth, I did feel a little faint before I fell... I've been very restless at night, having a lot of trouble sleeping lately. I guess I haven't had much of an appetite either. And that's been making me a little... weaker." He sounded solemn admitting all that, but it also seemed like saying it out loud lifted a small weight off his shoulders.

* * *

Peter and Mikayla came back inside, and Lorraine taught Peter and Anne how to change the dressing on Jim's wound. That way, they would be able to change it in between her home visits. She told them she would also be discussing medications with Jim's doctor. One of the medications would help settle Jim down, reduce his anxiety and help him sleep better. The other would be for pain.

"I don't want to get all loopy on drugs," Jim said.

"I completely understand," Lorraine acknowledged. "And remember, if the medicine or anything about your treatment makes you feel unusual or uncomfortable, we will always respect your wishes. If you don't want to take medicine, you don't have to. But your pain is likely to increase at some point, and it's possible that your anxiety will too. So a time may come when you *do* consent to taking medication."

Jim reluctantly nodded in agreement. "If the pain gets any worse, maybe I will use a little. But I don't want to start off by taking any more than is necessary. That's very important to me."

"Of course. We'll go over dosing in detail with you and Anne and the rest of your family if you'd like, and we'll always be there to advise you on the appropriate amount. At the end of the day, you know your body better than anyone. So it's important that you learn to honestly express what kind of pain you're in, so that your family and I can help you get the relief you need."

Jim nodded, but Anne and Lorraine exchanged a look: they both knew that Jim hardly ever liked to admit when he was hurting. "You know," Lorraine said. "Pain isn't always easy to talk about. Especially not in a lot of detail. That's one of the reasons we ask patients to tell us how they feel on a scale from one to ten. But sometimes, even that can be hard."

Lorraine thought about something and smiled. "I've been doing this for a long time. And that was one of the very first things I learned as a nurse. I had this patient; a sweet, insightful little girl. Only nine years old." Jim couldn't help but think of Mikayla. He turned and watched his granddaughter playing by the window, looking out at the front yard.

"She was very sick," Lorraine continued. "And sometimes the pain got so bad that she couldn't even speak. But she was smart as a tack, and I never forgot what she told me. One day I was asking her what her pain level was, and she had this idea. She said that if she ever got to the point where she was unable to speak, she could always tell me how she felt by giving me a thumbs up or a thumbs down. That way, she'd always be able to tell me if she was feeling okay, or if she needed me to adjust her pain medication or anything else. From that point on, I knew that even when a patient is having trouble talking about their pain, whether they're in a medicated state or they're too weak to speak, they can always give me the thumbs up, or the thumbs down. No one should ever have to tolerate unnecessary pain or anxiety."

Jim nodded, softly adding, "That seems like a good rule of thumb." He smiled, and Lorraine chuckled along with him.

* * *

As Lorraine was leaving, Mikayla asked her, "How come you only brought one dog today? Last time you had *two* dogs. Where is Snowy?"

Lorraine was touched. "Oh wow, I'm very impressed that you remember her name!" She laughed and looked up, catching Peter's eye. He hadn't anticipated Mikayla's question, but he nodded to Lorraine as if to say, "*Might as well tell her. I guess we'll see how she takes it...*"

Lorraine sighed. "I'm very sad to say it, but Snowy died this week... She was getting old, and one night she just closed her eyes and didn't wake up. At least I know that she went very peacefully, at home, with me and Lance at her side."

"Do you think Snowy's in heaven with St. Francis?" Mikayla blurted out. "He's my favorite cause he loves and protects all the animals." Lorraine smiled and caught Peter's eye again. Peter was nodding, impressed. His daughter seemed to be processing the news pretty well.

"How's your other dog doing without him? Isn't he lonely?" Mikayla asked.

"Well," Lorraine said. "Right now Lance needs a lot of extra hugging and petting and attention. And you know what? That works for me, because I'm sad too. So I need him as much as he needs me. That's how we can help each other."

Mikayla nodded quietly. She seemed to be thinking about that very seriously. After a few seconds, she turned and walked over to her grandma, who was sitting on the couch. Without saying anything at all, Mikayla climbed into Anne's lap and threw her arms around her. Anne, surprised but grateful, hugged her granddaughter tight.

Lorraine and Peter exchanged one final glance. There were tears in both of their eyes.

Chapter Five

Church, Anyone?

Later that weekend, Anne and Jim were paid a visit by their daughter Patty.

"You know," Patty said, "they're doing a special service at my church on Sunday."

Jim raised his eyebrows, not really listening. "Oh," he said, "that sounds very nice."

Jim knew that his daughter was very close with her church. She was a Catholic, like her mother. Jim, a Protestant, hadn't set foot in church since Patty was just a kid. He didn't begrudge anyone for going to church. It just wasn't for him.

"It's called The Anointing of the Sick. It's a Healing Mass."

"Oh, that sounds lovely," said Anne. But Jim just nodded absently.

Patty knew that her dad didn't have much interest, but she barreled ahead with her pitch anyway. "I really wish you would come with me, Dad," Patty said. "Just this once."

Jim laughed, shaking his head. "You know me," he said. "I don't go for all of that." Anne raised an eyebrow at him, so Jim tried to say something enthusiastic. "But... I love that *you* love church!" He added hopefully. Judging by the look on his daughter's face, that obviously wasn't cutting it.

Patty sighed. "I know, I know. You were always the dad who never knelt in church," she laughed. "But I believe that we could all use His help right now... It would be, as they say, Divine help... And it would really mean a lot to me."

"I'm not even a Catholic," Jim protested.

"I know that, Dad. But this is for everyone. Anyone who needs God's help."

Jim never felt much guilt about not going to church, and he wasn't going to start feeling bad about it now. But nevertheless, he knew that church was a part of his kid's life that he didn't really share anymore. And oddly enough, the thought of spending a Sunday morning with his family all dressed up and out among the community suddenly didn't seem like such a ghastly idea after all. If putting a smile on his daughter's face was the only good that could come from this, well, that was good enough for him.

"Well," he said, "if it's so important to you... I guess I could make an appearance."

* * *

On Sunday morning, Jim, Anne and their daughters Kylee and Patty gathered together.

"I can't believe I'm walking into a Church again," Jim said. "It's been so long that I hope the roof doesn't fall in on me." The family laughed as they drove towards the church.

It was nice going into town on a bright and sunny morning, seeing everyone out and about. Jim was a little worried that their friends and neighbors might look at him with curiosity or concern; they knew he was not typically a churchgoing man. But everyone that Jim bumped into was happy just to see him there. And when they asked him how he was, and he told them he was just swell, nobody questioned him or batted an eyelash. Today, at least, that was the truth.

* * *

When they entered the church, they were greeted by a woman who asked if any of them were to be included amongst the sick. Patty told her, "We are all here with illnesses of our own." The woman told them each to write their name on a tag and place it above their hearts. "Our priest will be praying for each of you by name as he anoints you with the holy oil," she explained, and directed them to their seats.

It was a solemn Mass. Some of the congregation even cried at times. When the deacon asked the congregation, "In the words of St. James, is anyone among you sick?" Patty smiled. She knew in her heart that this was where they were all meant to be. She was even happier that her father was there with her.

When it came time for Jim to be anointed, the priest laid his hands on Jim's head, and the deacon placed his hands above Jim's shoulders. At that moment, everyone in the church raised one hand, holding it out towards Jim. Jim was filled with a great warm feeling, and a look of peace came over him. It was in that moment that he, too, realized that this was just where he needed to be.

It struck Jim some time later that the laying on of hands during the "Anointing of the Sick" shared some similarities with Lorraine's practice of Compassionate Touch. Jim wondered how the other parishioners would react if they knew he and Anne had gotten into Reiki recently. *Wouldn't that surprise 'em?* he chuckled to himself.

As they left the church, Patty hugged her dad. "Thanks for indulging me Dad," Patty said. "I don't know how you feel, but I feel much better." Jim reacted with his usual smirk of a smile, never letting on how happy he was to be there.

Chapter Six

Therapeutic Touch

The following day Lorraine went over to Jim's house. When she asked Jim how his weekend had been, he mentioned his visit to church. "My first Mass in years. Patty convinced me to go," he said, smiling across the room at his daughter, who had swung by to bring over some lunch.

Lorraine took Jim's vitals and showed Patty how to change his bandages. Afterward, Jim went in for his afternoon nap, and Lorraine started to gather her things.

"That's nice you took your dad to church," she told Patty. "It sounds like he appreciated it."

"Well, getting him in there was the real miracle," Patty laughed. "I know he was just humoring me, but still, I'm glad he came with us. *Surprised*, but glad."

Lorraine nodded. "You know a lot of my patients are not religious, and sometimes at this stage of life, many of them find that going to a Mass or talking with a faith leader can be very therapeutic, even if it's for the first time."

"Have you ever seen someone turn to religion at the very end?"

"I have. I'll tell you a story if you'd like to hear it." Patty nodded, inviting Lorraine to sit down on the couch with her. Then Lorraine began to tell her story.

"I used to work the night shift," Lorraine said. "One night I was sent to check on a new patient. I show up to the house and the patient's wife answers the door. She's a bit frazzled because one of her sons is locked in his room; the other has just injured himself playing outside, and both kids are anxious because their father is dying. On top of this, she says, 'And now my husband is panicking that he's not going to get into heaven... See, he was born and raised Catholic, but since we met he's never been to church or even really *talked* about religion. And now that he's dying, he's suddenly talking about Jesus and he's afraid that he won't get into heaven...' The man's wife tells me she's not Catholic and she doesn't know what to do. She says 'I called a priest at his request, but the priest said he was having some kind of personal emergency and would have to send someone else in the morning. So now my husband's afraid that if he dies tonight, he won't get into heaven.' And then she says, 'I can't do this right now. So I need you to go into his room and pray with him.'

"Now, I'm a nurse, not a priest. I've never met this woman or her husband before tonight, and they have no idea whether or not I'm religious or spiritual. But I can see that they need this from me, so I don't say any of that. I just go into his room. As a hospice nurse part of my job *is* to discuss the patient's faith and spirituality. We want to be open and leave a space for any customs or rituals the patient wants to participate in during their last days. So I go to his bedside and offer to lead him in a meditation. I give him some reiki, and I ask him to meditate on nature, on his breathing, on stillness. He grows silent. His breathing starts to calm, and it's getting slower, and slower...

"Suddenly his eyes spring open, tears of joy spilling down his cheeks, and he looks at me with this reverence, total peace and calm and joy in his face and in his voice. And he tells me, 'I saw the face of Jesus. I'm no longer afraid. I know where I'm going now.' The next morning, the priest comes to his home, and the man tells him of his vision. The priest is shaken by this story, just as moved as the patient was. And then the priest confesses to the patient that he himself had been having a crisis of faith the previous evening. That was why he had delayed his visit until today. But now, just hearing this patient's story had restored the priest's faith. A few days later, the priest delivered this sermon at the man's funeral, and shared this story with the entire congregation, perhaps in turn bolstering their own faith..."

"Wow," Patty said, touched by Lorraine's story. "It's wild talking to you about all this; I actually thought of you when we were in church yesterday... It was a special Mass they were holding called the Anointing of the Sick. At one point, they do what's called 'the laying on of hands.' The priest laid his hands on each of our heads while the deacon placed his hands just above our shoulders. And I couldn't help but think of what I've seen you do for my dad. Compassionate Touch, I think you called it?" Lorraine nodded, and Patty continued. "Maybe this is a bit of a stretch, but I wondered if there was some connection between what they did in church yesterday and the sort of work you've been doing with my dad?"

Lorraine thought about this for a moment, pleasantly surprised by the question. "I think you may be right about that," she said. "It's an ancient healing practice that's been around for centuries. And it's used all around the world: China, Egypt, India, Tibet... It goes by a lot of different names, but the root of it is the same. In Christianity, they call it the laying on of hands, as you said. Jewish and Muslim people practice it as well. In the secular world it's often called Compassionate Touch, Therapeutic Touch or Healing Touch. In Japan they call it Reiki."

"I've heard about Reiki," Patty said. "What is it exactly?"

"Well the essential idea is that everyone and everything has a universal life energy. I mean, we know that all living things consume and burn energy. And when we're happy and healthy, that energy flows freely. But when we're injured or stressed or sick, it causes an imbalance. Reiki is about balancing that energy, promoting deep relaxation that allows our body's innate healing systems to work better.

It's often used during the end of life to ease the patient's pain, tension, fears… giving them a sense of calm and harmony."

"Huh," Patty said, cocking her head. "So it's some sort of… human energy field?"

Lorraine grinned. "It may sound kind of strange at first, but think about it. Don't you ever feel like you can sense someone's energy? It's like when you notice somebody looking at you even if you can't see them in your periphery. Or the way you can tell someone's mood even if they're not speaking or using explicit body language. Sometimes, you just get a vibe from people. People with gloomy thoughts will throw off a very different energy from somebody who's loving and healthy. Some people exude health and confidence, and some people don't. When you're walking down the street, take notice. If you pay attention, you can pick up on these subtle differences in everyone's energy, radiating from every individual."

"Sort of like their aura?"

"Exactly. Some people call it your aura, or your life force. In Chinese philosophy and medicine, they call it your 'Qi,' which sounds like 'chee' but is spelled Q-I."

Patty nodded, giving this some thought. "I've never really thought about it that way. I guess it makes sense when you think about it. I mean, everyone has electrical activity in their brain, right?"

"Exactly," Lorraine nodded, pleased. "And we can read those brain waves with an EEG, to see if they're normal or abnormal. Just like an EKG, which measures the electrical activity of the heart. So when we pour our love and energy into somebody, they generally respond well… So when I practice Compassionate Touch, first I clear my mind, then I focus all of my attention on the person in front of me, and I use my hands to help direct that energy to the patient."

"It does sound a little mysterious," Patty said. "But when I heard my dad say how relaxed and comfortable it made him, I knew I had to learn more. Just knowing that he is willing to allow you to try a new approach for pain relief on him is a great feat in and of itself. Did you study this as a nurse?"

Lorraine shook her head. "Well, I learned a bit about it when I was in nursing school, and then I continued researching it myself. Traditionally they don't always teach Reiki or holistic medicine to nursing students, but lately it's being taught more and more, and it's my hope that someday all medical professionals will have some kind of training or at least exposure to these practices."

"I'm surprised that more doctors and nurses don't practice it. I'm sure there are a lot of patients that are resistant to pain medication, and I'm sure many of them could benefit from it. Have you ever thought about teaching this stuff?"

Lorraine sighed, savoring the idea. "I would *love* to. It's always been a dream of mine to teach, but I don't know if I could really juggle teaching and Reiki with my hospice work. And right now, I feel like hospice is where I'm meant to be. Maybe someday though," she said hopefully.

Chapter Seven

Neighbors Helping Neighbors

Ever since Jim's fall, Anne had been trying to get him to use the wheelchair. At first, Jim had refused. But lately he had begun to lose his appetite, and with that came a feeling of weakness. Although he spent most of his time at home sitting in his favorite lounge chair, the best part of his day was when he would take Brandy for a long stroll around the neighborhood each morning. Anne offered to take the dog for her morning walk, but Jim didn't want to give up his sacred routine. So he promised his wife that from now on, he would use the wheelchair whenever he took Brandy out.

But this proved to be more difficult than he'd expected. Brandy was constantly getting the leash all tangled in the wheels, and Jim had to get in and out of the chair whenever he tried to clean up after her. It was during one of these frustrating excursions that Jim was approached by his neighbor Ryan, who had helped Jim get home after his last fall. "Hey, Mr. A.," he said. "Could you use a hand?"

Jim always had a fondness for Ryan and his family, ever since they moved into the house next door, back when Ryan was just an infant. Over the years Jim had watched Ryan grow up into a kind, thoughtful young man. A couple years back, Ryan's father became ill and passed away quite suddenly. Jim knew it must have been hard for Ryan and his mom, so over the next couple years he grew even closer with them, inviting them over for dinners, helping out around their house, even attending Ryan's baseball games now that Ryan's father was no longer cheering him on from the stands. In time, Jim and Ryan had come to treat each other like family.

"You know," Ryan said. "I'm always free in the morning before school. If you'd like, I'd be happy to go with you when you take Brandy for a walk."

Jim was touched. "That's very thoughtful of you, but I can't ask you to do that. You're too busy."

"Hey, if I don't do it, Brandy will probably drag you out of the house herself," Ryan said. They both laughed, and Jim accepted Ryan's generous offer.

* * *

Ryan was as good as his word, even better. For the next two weeks, he showed up every morning with a thermos of coffee to take Jim and Brandy for their daily walk. They talked about everything, from sports to Ryan's future and life in general. One day, during a silent moment, Jim quietly said "I'm gonna miss these walks."

"Me too. I don't know what I'm gonna do when you're gone."

"Oh nonsense," Jim said. "You've got your whole life ahead of you. You're going back to college in the fall, you're a great ball player, and I bet you've got lots of girlfriends," he said with a chuckle.

"Ha," Ryan laughed awkwardly, red in the face. "Sort of. Not really."

Ryan was quiet for a while as he pushed Jim's wheelchair down the street. Finally, he cleared his throat and spoke up. "Mr. A? I think I have to tell you something, but… I don't know how you're going to take it. It's just that… When my dad died, there were some things I wanted to say to him, but I never really worked up the courage. Ever since then you've been kind of like a second father to me, and I don't want to make the same mistake again."

Jim looked at him, concerned. "You know you can tell me anything."

Ryan was still pushing Jim's wheelchair along the sidewalk, so he didn't have to make eye contact while he spoke. "Um…. I *have* actually been seeing someone, but… not a girlfriend. It's a guy. His name is Ian. And uh, I guess I wanted to tell you that I'm gay. I hope that doesn't make you see me any different."

Jim turned around and smiled at him. "Of course not. The most important thing to me is that you're happy."

Ryan sighed deeply, realizing that he'd been holding his breath. "Thank you... I think I really needed to hear that. I didn't want to hide it from you and... I'm just gonna miss you, is all. It's gonna be really hard for me not having you around anymore."

"Well," Jim said, patting Ryan's hand, "if Ian's half the guy you deserve, he'll be there to help you through."

Ryan looked surprised. "Do you think that would be okay? I mean, If I brought him when it's time to... you know... say goodbye?" Jim realized he was talking about the funeral. "I mean, I still haven't figured out how I'm gonna tell my mom. I'm afraid she's gonna be really upset with me."

Jim stopped the chair and turned to face Ryan. He looked him in the eye and said calmly and clearly: "You tell her whenever you feel ready. But I *know* that your mom *and* your dad would both say the same thing I'm telling you now: you're a fine young man, and I'm so very proud of you." Ryan nodded, overcome with gratitude. Jim reached out to him with both arms, and they hugged.

Chapter Eight
The Decline

Jim and his family reminded themselves and each other that every day was a gift, but the difficult truth was that with each passing day, Jim's health seemed to decline significantly. It was becoming more and more evident that no matter how hard he tried to fight it, Jim was losing the battle to cancer. One morning, Jim woke up light-headed and found that he was unable to stand. When Anne discovered Jim in this weakened condition, she immediately called Lorraine. Anne was instructed to keep him in bed and was told that help was on the way.

After speaking with Anne, Lorraine was convinced that the situation had taken a turn for the worse. She quickly went about calling all of Jim's principal caretakers. There was his primary doctor, the always helpful nurse practitioner there, and of course Shanice. After much discussion and airing of concerns, it was decided that it was time to take the next steps. In due time, the family was alerted to their father's changing circumstances and one by one, they began to show up at the house. There, they were greeted by Shanice and Lorraine. They had come together, a welcome but worrying sign.

Shanice explained, "Lorraine and I decided to make a joint visit today just in case any of you had any questions."

Peter nodded, a gesture of stoicism masking a tidal wave of concern. A lump formed in his throat, but he swallowed it down. At last he said, "We've all seen the changes in Dad. Lord knows Mom has.

But I think we all need to hear what you have to say."

Jim was asleep in his bed as Anne and her children gathered in the living room with Lorraine and Shanice. As it dawned on the family that the end was rapidly approaching, Lorraine began to gently prepare them for the new challenges that Jim would be facing.

"I've spoken with Jim's doctor's office. Collectively, we agreed that now is the time to have this conversation." Lorraine paused for a moment, then continued. "The dying process isn't the same for everyone. You may begin to notice Jim experiencing some physical and emotional changes, so we've prepared a list of some of the things he may experience. Try not to get caught up in *looking* for these changes, as he probably won't undergo all of them. But it's good to be aware and prepared for the changes that *do* arise." Shanice handed out packets titled "Preparing Papers." The family read through the list:

Physical Changes:

- Increased pain
- Lots of sleeping/fatigue
- Disorientation/confusion
- Nausea/vomiting
- Incontinence/constipation
- A decrease in appetite and lack of fluid intake
- A decrease in urine output
- Restlessness/anxiety/agitation
- Irregular breathing pattern/shortness of breath
- The coolness of hands, arms, feet, and legs
- Darkening of the coloring of the extremities
- Congestion/gurgling

Emotional Changes:

- Withdrawal from loved ones
- Vision-like experiences and visions of previously deceased people they once knew
- Duality: preparing to move from this existence into the next dimension of life, each in his/her unique way

After reviewing the Preparing Papers, Shanice turned to Anne. "I understand that Jim has fallen twice now," she said. "It may be time to think about getting some extra help. Our services could provide you with a Hospice Aide. That would be my recommendation. Our aides are incredible, compassionate care-givers, and many of our patients are deeply appreciative of all that they do for them. Or you may want to consider hiring a full-time caregiver."

Anne hesitated. "Thank you, but I don't think my husband would accept round-the-clock care. It's never been Jim's nature to burden anyone... At the same time, I know he doesn't want to burden me or the kids, so maybe he *would* be receptive to someone helping for a few hours a week..."

Shanice nodded. "Why don't you talk about it with Jim, and if you decide that you could use the help, I'll put in the request for a home-health aide right away." Reluctantly, she added "Do you think he'd be open to accepting a hospital bed now?"

Shaking her head, Anne said, "I don't know. That's going to be difficult for him. He's a proud man." Shanice nodded and gently placed her hand on Anne's shoulder. On some level, she understood her pain.

Just then, Jim woke up. Anne and Lorraine went into his bedroom. Since the rest of the family was in the living room, Lorraine decided that this was a good moment to speak privately with Jim and Anne.

"I wanted to ask if you've given any more thought to the DNR form."

Anne looked towards Jim and held his hand. "We have. We needed some time to think about it and discuss it with the kids, but we've made our decision now."

Jim patted her hand and turned to Lorraine. "We gave our consent for the DNR. We've signed the forms and let the whole family know."

Lorraine sympathized with their decision, knowing that it could not have been easy to make. She told them she would send one copy to Jim's doctor for him to sign, and leave the other form with them. She suggested that they hang it on the refrigerator or a cabinet, so that it would be visible and accessible to all healthcare personnel and EMT workers in case they were called. Anne nodded, but Jim felt that she was trembling. He turned to her and smiled, reminding her that this was what they had both decided, and that it was the right choice for them.

* * *

Over the next few days, it became more challenging for Jim to move around on his own. He would run out of breath quite frequently, and often needed others to support him. So he began to spend most of his time in the den, or in his bed upstairs with Anne. Lorraine and the hospice staff were there to ease Jim and the family into this next phase. Lorraine set up the oxygen tank and taught them how and when to use it, and a hospital bed was delivered and set up in the den.

Jim's pride would not allow his children to help him with his daily personal care, so he asked Shanice to request a home-health aide, and soon came to sincerely appreciate their help. In addition to helping him with bathing, shaving and other personal needs, they would help get him into the den in the morning, and into his bed when he was feeling tired. Jim enjoyed the aide's visits and valued all of their help. Anne was also grateful for them, and even a little envious of their ability to make the bed so perfectly that you couldn't tell that anyone had ever slept there. Shanice suggested adding a volunteer to the team, someone who could stay with Jim and give Anne the chance to get out of the house. Anne knew that things were getting difficult and accepted the extra help without a moment's hesitation.

Anne and Jim were fortunate to have a family who lived close by, with children that could pitch in whenever they were asked, but without the help of the hospice staff, the home health aide, and the volunteers, they knew it would never have been possible for Jim to spend his final weeks and days in the comfort of his own home.

Chapter Nine

The Family Comes Together

It was a cool but sunny morning as Ryan crossed the street towards Jim's house with his thermos of coffee in hand. He hadn't had much sleep, but he was full of energy nonetheless. He had some exciting news to share with Jim; after their big talk, he had finally worked up the courage to tell his mother about his boyfriend, Ian. She took the news just as well as Jim had. Ryan wasn't sure what he had been so afraid of, and now that he had gotten the truth off his chest, he knew that he had Jim to thank. But when he arrived at the house, he was surprised to see Anne answer the door.

"Jim's still sleeping," she explained. "He's not feeling too good these days."

"Aw, that's too bad," Ryan said. He was surprised to hear that Jim was still sleeping. It was definitely a worrisome sign, considering Jim was always the early bird in the neighborhood. But Ryan decided not to say anything that might further upset Mrs. A. She looked like she'd been having a tough few days herself. "Well, I'm happy to take Brandy for a walk anyway," Ryan offered.

Anne considered it for a moment. She could simply hand the leash to Ryan and go back to bed for another half hour. She hadn't been sleeping too well herself. But as she looked out on the sunny street, she decided a walk would do her some good.

"Oh, I can take her," Anne said. "I should get out of the house for a little while anyway."

"I'll join you, if that's okay," Ryan said.

Anne smiled, touched. "That would be lovely," she said.

Jim awoke to the sound of the front door closing. He looked out his bedroom window and saw Anne and Ryan walking the dog down the street, chatting and laughing together. It was good to see Anne taking her mind off his health for a minute. He hated to see her worry, and wished that he could do more to put her mind at ease. But that was impossible; he didn't have much time left, and they both knew it. There was no way to slow down the future, but at least he could try to take care of as many things as he could before his time was up. The next chapter of Anne's life would not be easy, but he would see to it that she would at least be comfortable and cared for with all of her affairs in order.

* * *

"Peter," Jim said shortly after his son swung by for his morning visit, "bring me out to the patio if you can. I have a few things I want to talk to you about." Peter nodded. His dad sounded serious, but Peter was glad to hear him talking this way. Maybe his father looked a little skinny and a little pale, but today he sounded like himself, like a man on a mission. As Peter wheeled his father towards the back door, Jim turned towards him. "And bring a pen and paper. You may want to write some of this down." Peter smiled. That was his old man, alright.

"The sun feels good," Jim said, sighing in pleasure and closing his eyes.

Peter watched his dad patiently. He knew they had some business to discuss, but for now he was enjoying the peaceful silence. For a moment, he was able to put aside all of the context of this conversation, forget about the cancer and the nurses and the dying process. For *just* a moment, he was simply sharing a quiet moment with his father on the sunny patio as he had done thousands of times in his life. For just *one single* moment, life felt blissfully mundane again.

Finally, Jim spoke. "Peter, there are things that I need you to take care of for your mother. All of this worrying about her is keeping me up at night."

"Sure, Dad. You name it," Peter replied.

"Well, first of all, the bathroom needs to have the grout replaced. I need you to get some estimates. Then you have to hire someone to put railings up, and a second set of stairs around the patio. I have the blueprints that I made for the guy who did the front railings, but he never finished the job so… Just make sure that you hire a good contractor. And… I believe that ought to do it."

"Is that all?" Peter asked. He was surprised; he thought there would be a longer list of unfinished business. "I can take care of all that," he said.

"And just…" Jim began, shutting his eyes tight, "*Please*: Look after your mother when I'm gone. You kids have been so helpful, and we appreciate it so much. But when all this is over, don't stop visiting. I don't want her to be…" Jim trailed off, unable to finish.

"She's not gonna be alone," Peter said, putting a hand on his father's shoulder. "We're not going anywhere." Jim nodded, a quiet expression of gratitude on his face.

The two men sat in silence for a while as Jim closed his eyes, taking in all the sun that he could, not knowing if it may be his last time.

* * *

There was still one more important piece of business to discuss, and this was clearly the best time to bring it up. All four of Jim's children were coming over for Sunday dinner, and he thought they should all be present. With the home-health aide and the volunteers helping Jim out, Anne was able to put together a feast. It was a wonderful dinner, despite a few small disappointments; Patty was unsuccessful in her efforts to get everyone to say grace, Jimmy was unsuccessful in his attempt to inspire his father to make a toast, and Anne was unsuccessful in her last-ditch effort to turn Jim into a fan of brussel sprouts. But aside from these minor setbacks, it was a marvelous evening, full of laughter and memories and tender moments. After dinner, Jim cleared his throat nervously, trying to barrel through this last bit of business without too much sentimentality.

"I'm glad that the six of us have this time together. I do want to go over a few things with all of you. I need you to know where to find everything, and I need you to know where things stand financially. I'm telling you this so that you can help your mother. I already met with my lawyer to finalize everything, so hopefully that will make things a bit easier for all of you." Jim then told the family what banks his accounts were in, what broker he used, and where to find all of his important papers. "And that's that," he concluded, tapping his fingers on the table like he was playing the piano. His family sat in silence.

Patty began to cry. "We don't want to know about your finances, Dad. We just want you."

"No, no," Jim responded firmly. "There'll be none of that; stop." He looked down, trying to ignore the sudden pain in his abdomen, trying not to let his emotions show, wishing away the uncomfortable scene. But his family knew what he was feeling and why they were having this conversation now.

Jim was accepting the inevitable, accepting that it would come *soon*, and he was trying to let his family do the same.

* * *

An inconvenient and often sad truth about those in hospice care or on their way along that journey, is that when their time comes, it isn't necessarily the best time for everyone else. We all have our commitments, and the struggle to know how best to use and allocate our time is a universal one. So for every family member that is able to sit by the bed of a suffering loved one, there are usually several others that aren't even able to be in the same state.

After dinner, Kylee and her father sat down in the den. Everyone else was going home or going to bed, but Kylee and her father kept the conversation going. They talked about the family for a while, about each other, about life. Jim asked her how work was going. She told him honestly that it was a bit stressful at the moment; she was supposed to fly out of state for an important three-day business trip, but she was cancelling it because she wanted to stay at home with him.

"No! You're going!" He insisted firmly, surprising her. "Do *not* cancel the trip."

Kylee shook her head. "But it's too long to be away right now! They're just going to have to find someone else to replace me."

"Nonsense," Jim said. "Haven't I raised you right? What have I *always* told you and Patty and the boys? Once you make a commitment, you are obligated to follow through. You told them they could count on you, and they're counting on you now."

"But Dad, this is different!" exclaimed Kylee. "You're counting on me too, and… and I'd rather spend this time here with you."

"Kylee. It's only three days. You love this job. I don't want you missing an important trip on my account."

"I don't know, Dad. Maybe you're right, but… what if something happens while I'm away?"

Jim softened his tone. "Listen to me, Kylee. Please. You have *always* been here for me. I could never forget that. I just don't want you to stop living *your* life just because *I'm*…" Jim trailed off.

Kylee broke down and sobbed in her father's arms, something she hadn't done since she was a little girl. "Dad, I love you more… more than I can say. I really do… I love you. I love you so much." She wiped her tears away, but she still seemed unsure. "I guess it's only three days… Like you said. So… I'll be back soon, okay?"

Jim smiled down at her. "Don't worry, Kylee. Just remember, I love you no matter *where* you are, and your love always travels back to me."

* * *

In the other room, Patty's phone rang. It was her son, Bobby. It wasn't unusual for him to call so late. He'd been calling more often to check in on his grandfather. But this time, when he asked her "how's Grandpa doing?" his mother's response had changed considerably.

"Not good," Patty said reluctantly. "I think it's almost time…" She trailed off with a mournful sigh. There was a pause. "Bobby? Are you there?"

When her son responded, his voice cracked a little. But he sounded calm too, as if he'd been expecting this. "I guess I should start looking into flights for tomorrow," he said.

Patty felt a jolt of relief, but she didn't want to get carried away. "I don't know, Bobby. You just started that job --"

"It's okay, Mom. I told my boss this might happen and he's fine with it."

"But… I don't think Grandpa would want you to miss work. Plus, he's got me and your uncles and your aunt Kylee, you know. We're all here for him."

"Okay then," Bobby said. There was a pause in the conversation. Patty sighed. But then Bobby continued. "Well then… let me be there for *you*."

Patty got choked up. She shut her eyes as a wave of sadness, gratitude and pride washed over her. She'd raised him well, just like Bobby's grandparents had done for her. When Bobby said "Mom? Hello?" she cleared her throat and responded. "Okay, honey. I'll check the flights," she said. "Maybe you could leave after work tomorrow and your brother Brian can pick you up at the airport."

"That sounds good. I'll book something now and I'll see you tomorrow night."

"Thank you, Bobby," she said affectionately. "Have a safe trip, and you know the drill…call me before you take off *and* when you land."

"I know, I know, Mom!" Bobby laughed. "Get some sleep, okay? You sound tired."

"I will. I love you Bobby. See you tomorrow night."

* * *

When Brian picked Bobby up at the airport the following evening, they talked to their mom and decided it was too late at night. They would have to wait until the morning to visit. When they went over to their grandparents' house the following day, the whole spirit of the house lifted. Anne was overjoyed to see her two strapping grandsons together at the front door, a welcome addition to the usual cast of characters. They hugged tightly, and Anne looked up at her grandsons. "Bobby and Brian, I swear you two are still growing!"

"We stopped growing *years* ago, Grandma," Brian laughed.

"You know," Bobby added, "I never *feel* tall... Not until I see our family Christmas photo, anyway." Anne laughed and welcomed them inside. When they entered the den, Jim was in his wheelchair with his back to the door. Anne announced, "Jim! We have some surprise guests!"

While Bobby was happy and relieved to be back among his family, the sight of his grandfather in a wheelchair was a bit of a shock. His grandpa had always been strong and energetic, a vital and commanding presence in a room, and Bobby hardly ever thought of him as "old-looking." But the frail, tired man sitting in the wheelchair before him seemed to have lost twenty pounds and aged twenty years since Bobby's last visit.

But then Jim turned and a smile crept across his face; Bobby recognized in an instant the familiar glint in his grandfather's eye, and forgot all about the changes in his appearance. Bobby didn't often hug his grandfather, but now he reached over and gave him a big, long embrace.

"Bobby! What are you doing here?" Jim patted his back, laughing.

"Ah, I thought I'd swing by," Bobby joked.

"But didn't you just start your new job?" Jim asked, worried.

"Yes, and it's great. I love it… but it doesn't hold a candle to how much I love you guys!… Seriously, though, it's okay. They're very supportive and they all encouraged me to come." Jim still looked concerned, so Bobby tried to assure him. "Don't worry, Grandpa! They're not going to fire me… I'm too good at my job!"

Bobby's last line finally wiped the concerned look off his grandpa's face, and Jim burst out laughing. "That's my boy! That's my boy!" They chuckled until Jim's hearty laughter turned into a coughing fit. When he got it under control, he patted Bobby's arm. "I'm glad you're here, son," he said. Bobby smiled. "I'm glad I'm here too."

* * *

That night the whole family gathered for dinner. As they were finishing up, Brian said "Let's get a picture of all of us." His wife Amanda took out her cellphone and held it in front of all of them. "Say cheese!" she said, and snapped a photo.

"Hey Grandpa!" Brian blurted out. "You finally caught up with the times. Your first selfie!" Everyone had a good laugh then, Jim most of all.

At the end of the evening as Brian and Amanda said their goodbyes, she sent the picture to everyone in the family. Anne checked her cellphone and saw the picture. Almost everyone in the family was in it, all of them giving their best, warmest smiles. She clutched her phone to her chest. "This is a picture I'll treasure forever," she said.

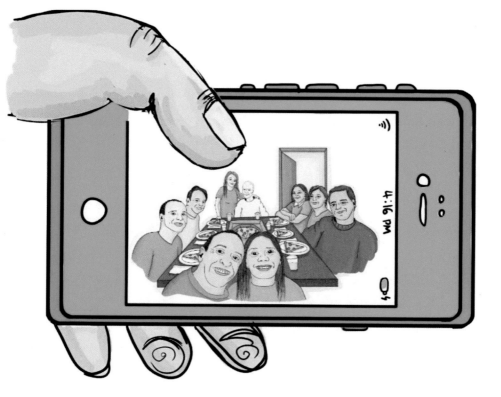

Chapter Ten

Rites And Rituals

The next morning, Anne served Jim his favorite breakfast: scrambled eggs, bacon, and a cup of strong coffee. Jim smiled warmly at her and took a bite, but after a little while, Anne realized he wasn't really eating, just pushing the food around on the plate with his fork.

"Sorry," he said. "Stomach's not feeling too good." Jim wasn't hungry at all. Part of the problem was that he had been constipated lately, and his stomach felt painfully full.

"How about a fruit cup?" Anne offered. Trying to make light of it, Jim replied, "No thanks, but Italian ice may do the trick!"

While Anne was getting the ice, Kylee entered the room, suitcase in tow. "Well, Jimmy's gonna drive me over to the airport in a few minutes," she said. She still seemed torn about her decision to leave, but her dad gave her a steady nod and a good firm hug. "I hate to be leaving, Dad," Kylee said. "I'm only going because you insisted."

She wouldn't let go of their hug. Jim patted her back. "I love you," he said. "Have a safe trip and don't forget to call us from the airport. You know your mother." He gave her a kiss on the cheek, and she finally pulled out of their tight embrace.

"I love you too, Dad. I'll see you in a few days." She hid a tear behind a weak smile.

Jimmy got Jim settled on the couch, and by the time he and Kylee left for the airport a few minutes later, his dad was already fast asleep. When Jimmy returned a few hours later, his mom was in the kitchen with Patty, and his father was still asleep in the den. He had hardly even changed positions.

"Hey mom?" He asked. "How long has Dad been sleeping?"

She replied, "It's been on and off all day, and he hasn't eaten much at all. I'm worried about him, but Lorraine is coming over soon. She'll know what to do."

* * *

Lorraine seemed concerned. She had been all smiles at the door, but within a few minutes of entering the house, she was looking down at Jim with her brow furrowed. They had tried to wake him, but he wouldn't even stir. "I'll just check his vitals," Lorraine said. "I don't want to disturb him." She proceeded to check his heart rate as usual, but Anne couldn't ignore the concern she had heard in Lorraine's voice. She realized she'd never seen worry in Lorraine's eyes. Compassion, yes. Sympathy, always, but never *worry*. This was new.

Anne had told her that Jim had been sleeping a lot; all night, and most of the day. He hadn't been eating much either, as he was having gastrointestinal issues. Furthermore, his mobility had continued to decline, and he wasn't doing any moving on his own now. Between the family, the volunteers and the home health aides, they'd been lifting him to and from his chair, the commode, the bath, the hospital bed in the den, and his own bed every night. Lorraine acknowledged that all this must be difficult.

"We do what we gotta do, you know," Jimmy assured her. "Family first."

Lorraine smiled softly. "Well it's a good thing he agreed to the hospital bed. From this point on, he probably won't be leaving it."

Lorraine had discussed Jim's health status with his doctor and the rest of the hospice team, and they had come up with a list of recommendations. Lorraine suggested the use of the oxygen tank and a suppository to help relieve the pressure in Jim's abdomen. She also suggested that they insert a catheter for urination, which would mean that the family wouldn't have to lift him every time he needed the bathroom. Finally, she said "We're all aware of how reluctant Jim has been to pain medication, but we'd suggest a low dose of Morphine. We'll only increase as needed, and collectively these other recommendations could help keep the morphine to a minimum, which is how he wants it to be."

Anne, Patty and Jimmy agreed that Jim could use the pain medication, the suppository and the oxygen. But they refused the catheter; Anne and her sons knew that Jim would be much more comfortable if he just continued with the urinal. "Hopefully," Anne said, "all this will bring him some relief."

The family seemed worried. They feared that Jim was entering a new phase now, that he would be passing soon. Lorraine said, "I have seen many families go through this, and it's never easy. Even when the families are estranged, there's always that one person, a doctor, a caregiver, a nurse, a best friend, a neighbor, or a casual acquaintance that makes a difference in their end-of-life care. In this case, Jim is surrounded by loved ones. He's truly blessed to have all of you here, and he's so proud of all of you. He tells me that every time we meet."

Anne began to cry, and Jimmy rubbed her back.

"I just don't know what to do," she said. "Do we just wait for him to go? Do we talk to him about his passing, or do we just pretend it isn't happening? Do we try to keep him awake, or let him sleep? I just want to make this as… peaceful as possible."

"Whether he's asleep or he isn't, whether he's talking or not, he can hear you, and he knows that you're here. Tell him you love him. Tell him you know he loves you too. Touch him in a way that's comforting to both of you. And based on what you've previously shared about your faith, you can tell him that you can feel God's love protecting him and you. Let him know that your trust is in God, that God will continue to support and take care of you long after he is gone, and that you will take care of each other. Let him know that you believe he will be at peace when he goes. Forgive him, if there is the need. And most importantly, permit him to let go. But how you spend this time, what you decide to say and not to say, is ultimately up to you."

"I guess everyone comes at this differently," Jimmy said.

"That's true," Lorraine said. "But death comes to all of us, and in general, it's my experience that the dying aren't interested anymore in putting on airs or trying to impress anyone. An Atheist once told me, 'I'm not scared to die. I think it's harder on the living.' When a patient speaks, what I hear, almost universally, is genuine and authentic. And something else seems to be universal – ritual, some sort of custom – is essential to the family. Ritual seems to elevate and dignify the occasion and also helps to make it all seem familiar."

Jimmy and Patty exchanged a look. "We've been debating that, I guess," Jimmy said. "We're Catholic, of course, but my dad was never much of a church-going man. Now we're trying to figure out how many of those rituals are appropriate to bring into all this."

The family sat in silence while they thought about this. Finally, Anne said. "I'm sure that you've seen many different things throughout your career. Maybe you can tell us about some other families and *their* experiences."

"I'd be happy to," said Lorraine.

* * *

"I remember two winters ago when a Jewish woman died during a terrible snowstorm. The family's Rabbi was unable to make it to the house to prepare the body. The son of the deceased woman lit a candle, placed it by her head, and led us all with prayers of forgiveness and reconciliation from the Torah. They prayed the Jewish prayer for the soul of the departed called El Maleh Rachamim. As we all joined in this prayer, the women of the family and I carefully bathed the woman's body. We then wrapped the body in a simple white shroud, called a Tachrichim. This Hebrew ritual of purification is called Taharah and is the act of preparing to meet your maker with a display of dignity and respect. It is a reminder that death is not the act of leaving this world, rather an arrival into a higher, a holier world. I marveled at how their faith prepared the body and then never left the deceased alone, while others followed through as tradition would have it, and covered all of the mirrors in the home as they prepared for their period of healing called Shiva. I noticed a red ribbon tied around her left wrist and asked about its relevance because I had seen it on patients of various faiths. Her son told me that it was custom to put it on the dying to ward off misfortune so they can move on to the higher world. The ritual, even without the Rabbi present, was so comforting to the family. I am ever so grateful that I was present for it.

"One of the most beautiful examples of deep faith and true love was of a Hindu patient of mine. She fell in love and married a non-Hindu. Upon entering her home for the first time, I couldn't help but notice photos of Hindu ceremonies and rituals hanging on the wall. As she was nearing the end of life, she told me that she felt she was not a good Hindu, because she had married outside of her faith. She did not believe that her soul would live on. I asked her if she had ever considered that perhaps there were many paths to God. She never answered me but simply smiled, then closed her eyes.

"On my next visit, a couple of days later, excitedly, the couple shared a picture that was taken a day prior and they explained to me what they had witnessed. She and her husband were sitting on the patio by their fire pit, and her husband asked her how he would know or what sign she would send him to tell him that her soul has lived on from above. And just then, an Indigo Bunting Blue Bird, representing messages from God, flew down from behind the woman and went up over their fireplace, thus sparking the flames as her husband caught it on camera. That bird was her father's sign for her, and at that moment they both knew that it would be her sign for her husband as well. She transitioned from this life to death surrounded by her family, and together they honored the Hindu Pran Sutra. It means 'Peace to the soul and may it proceed towards attaining freedom from this life to being reborn in the next.' She and her family were at peace when she died. The family then researched the meaning of the Indigo Bunting Blue Bird and found that the bird migrates at night and is continuously aligned with a star as it navigates its way in the darkness. This sent chills up and down our arms.

"I found it quite interesting that while Hindus use fire to communicate with the Gods, I have learned that the seven major religions of Buddhism, Christianity, Confucianism, Hinduism, Islam, Judaism, and Taoism all share a commonality. Each uses prayer and cleansing rituals as a sign of respect in preparation for a higher, holier place."

Lorraine continued, "I believe that everyone at some point in their life is on a spiritual journey. I just try to meet them wherever they are. I know that their journey and mine are different and that they have different beliefs than I do. No matter who they are, I feel the energy of love, compassion, and understanding when I am with a family.

"I also know that I am just so blessed to have been called to this job. Nurses so often get called on to go the extra mile for families, and for the most part, we feel honored to do it. I won't go on with any more stories; nonetheless, I just want to reiterate what Shanice said: 'Give him all the love you can, say whatever you need to say, let nothing go unsaid.' Simply put, have no regrets. Talk about great memories and times spent together, even if it appears as if he is sleeping because he is still aware of what is going on around him.

Don't stop talking to him, and if you see his breathing change, don't be afraid to tell him that it's okay to die. He needs to hear that from you, and that will make it easier for him to let go of this life."

After Lorraine left, Jimmy and Patty helped their father back into his bedroom, and laid him down in his bed. Lorraine had said that it may make more sense to keep him in his hospital bed in the den, but Jim's children knew that this was very likely the last night their parents would ever spend in bed together. They had shared this bed for over sixty years. Most nights they had crawled into that bed next to each other without even thinking about it, but that was their ritual, a practice more sacred than anything else, one they had shared together forever.

* * *

Before going to sleep that night, Patty went to her mother's room and sat on the edge of the bed. Anne said, "I sit here and hold his hand, and I feel helpless. I can't do anything for him."

"Mom. You and Dad have been married for sixty wonderful years," Patty responded gently. "In that time you've done so much for one another, and so much for all of us. Now is your time to just sit here and be with him. That's all he needs from you right now." There was a brief silence, then Patty reached into her bag and said "There's something that I wanted to do for Dad, if it's okay with you." She removed a religious item from her bag. "Do you remember what this is? It's called a scapular. We're supposed to place it around his neck."

Anne cocked her head. "What is it for exactly? I'm trying to remember."

"It was a gift from the Heavenly Mother, bearing the message 'Whosoever dies in this garment shall not suffer eternal fire.' "

Anne hesitated. "Are you sure, honey? You know your father isn't Catholic."

"I know. But ever since he came with us to church, I feel like he's been more open to this sort of thing. I asked him if I could place this prayer shawl on his chair, and he actually seemed grateful for it. And earlier, when he was feeling agitated, he let me burn some incense and it really calmed him down... I know he's not really religious, but my priest and even Lorraine said that rituals like this can bring a huge relief to the patient and their families. And *this* is what I believe. This is *my* ritual. And I want to share it with him."

Anne agreed to let her place it on Jim. "If your father was awake right now, he would be grateful for this. He's so proud of you." And together, they began to pray the Divine Mercy Chaplet.

Chapter Eleven
The Art Of Letting Go

Then came the visitors. Word of Jim's health had spread around the community, and several of Jim's neighbors and friends came by the following day to pay him one last visit. In the morning, Jim's sons brought him into the hospital bed in the den where he was surrounded by family. By the afternoon, Jim and Anne were showered with handmade cards written by two little girls from the neighborhood named Claire and Evie. Ryan and his mother came to offer their condolences and bring a few home-cooked meals. Even Jim's doctor came to visit. He sat with Anne and they spoke all about the last couple of months, and though he was saddened to see Jim in this state, he was glad that he had steered them in the right direction, and that hospice care had given the family some dignity in this final chapter of Jim's life. Everyone who came into the den would sit there quietly, sometimes speaking to Jim, sometimes with their heads bowed in prayer or deep reflection. The visitors came and went, but Jim slept through it all, lying peacefully in the hospital bed with his beloved Boxer curled up at his feet. Brandy had always been infinitely social, but on this day, every time the doorbell rang and someone new came or left, she never once left Jim's side.

The final visitor that day was the church pastor. Shanice the social worker had called him at the family's request and arranged a visit. Pastor Nick arrived just as the sun was setting that evening. He introduced himself to the family and was brought into the den to see Jim. Knowing that it was difficult for Jim to speak, he quietly said a prayer over him. As Pastor Nick prayed, the slightest trace of a smile appeared on Jim's lips, and he sighed deeply. Without words, Jim had acknowledged and accepted the meaningful words of the pastor, knowing that his time on Earth was limited. The pastor sat with Jim for a while, then spoke with the rest of the family. He hugged Anne, told them to call if they needed him, and left.

Patty decided that she would once again spend the night with her parents, so she told her sons to head home. Before leaving for the night, Bobby and Brian and his wife each spent a moment alone with their grandfather and told him that they loved him. Jim struggled to repeat the words back to them, but Bobby and Brian knew that his love for them was eternal, even if he couldn't say it.

* * *

Kylee called Patty that night. She had tried getting through to their mother earlier, but Anne hadn't answered. As soon as Patty picked up the phone, Kylee blurted out the question that had been on her mind every moment of her business trip: "How is Dad?"

"Not well," Patty said, fighting back tears. "All he's doing is sleeping. I -- I don't know how long he has left..."

Kylee swallowed a lump in her throat. "I'll be on the next flight. Let me book something and I'll call you right back."

Patty heard her dad mumbling in the other room. "Don't hang up yet," Patty said. "I'm gonna try putting you on speaker. He's awake on and off, but at least he'll hear your voice."

She brought the phone into the other room and held it near her father's face.

"Dad?" Patty said. "Kylee's on the phone."

Struggling to speak, Kylee said, "Hi Dad..." There was no answer. Kylee's voice began to waver. "I'm on my way to the airport now. Just hang on, okay? I'll see you soon."

Jim's eyes were closed, but his voice was clear and strong as he spoke the first words he had said that evening. "I love you, Kylee."

* * *

Jim stayed in the hospital bed that night, and Anne slept on the couch right beside him. She tried to hold Jim's hand, but he kept moving away from her. His breathing sounded shallow and raspy, and occasionally he moaned. He spoke a couple of times, but it wasn't clear what he was saying. Sometimes it was just hard to hear him, but at other times he seemed to be speaking unintelligibly, like he was having a strong fever dream. Patty heard some of her father's moaning, and she came into the den.

"Hey Mom, is he okay?"

Anne looked up, deeply upset. "He won't let me touch him... We *always* hold hands. I just don't understand, and I don't like the sound he's making when he breathes. What's happening?" She turned her worried gaze back to her husband. "Oh honey, please let me know if you are in pain. I don't want you to be in any pain..." But Jim could only reply with a deep, rattling breath.

Patty could hear how distressed her mother was. Anne was worried that Jim was having trouble breathing, that the oxygen tank wasn't working properly, that he was hurting. Wanting to make sure that her father was comfortable and that her mother's mind was at ease, Patty called the hospice center. Thankfully she was told that Lorraine was on the night shift tonight, and would be over shortly.

* * *

By the time Lorraine arrived about forty-five minutes later, she found Jim sleeping peacefully in the den. Anne and Patty were sitting by his side, and Brandy was curled around his feet.

"I tried to get her off the bed," Anne explained, gesturing toward the dog, "but she just won't leave his side."

Lorraine smiled softly. "I wouldn't be surprised if, on some level, Brandy could sense that the end is near."

"Really?" Anne asked, surprised.

"There is a nursing home near here," Lorraine explained, "They have a house cat named Cloey. The staff knows that if you pay attention to the room that Cloey stays in during the night, there is a good chance that the patient in that room won't make it till morning. Do all cats and dogs know? I'm not sure, but Cloey does. It's the same with some people, I suppose. There are those who won't go into a room when someone is about to take their last breath, so they stand vigil outside the room while others go to the bedside. Everyone reacts differently when death is approaching, but animals are particularly in touch with those instincts. Do they sense a loss of vitality? Do they smell something? No one knows. But they often seem to have a sense about these things."

Lorraine took Jim's vitals and checked that the oxygen was flowing freely from the tank. Jim stirred in his sleep. He opened his eyes, mumbling softly. His gaze drifted between the three women at his bedside, and he closed his eyes again.

"Jim, can you let us know if you're in pain?" Lorraine asked. He groaned in response. They sighed, accepting that Jim was unable to respond. But then Lorraine looked down at his hand. He was giving her a thumbs-up. On his face was the slightest trace of a smile.

* * *

Everyone breathed a sigh of relief. "Okay," Lorraine said. "At least he's not in any pain. And I've checked the oxygen tank. It's working fine. His lungs are just working a lot harder right now."

Anne looked at her husband and reached down for his hand, but he moved it away from her again. Upset, she stood up and left the room. Patty and Lorraine followed her into the kitchen, where they found Anne crying. "Why won't he hold my hand?" She asked softly. "He's always held my hand…"

"He may be trying to let go," Lorraine said gently.

Anne turned to Lorraine, upset and confused.

"You give him energy, life-force, love," Lorraine said. "Sometimes, when somebody's dying, and their loved ones are talking to them and touching them, that energy is the only thing really keeping them there."

"Really? I've never heard that before," Anne said, wiping a tear. Lorraine's words were already giving her some comfort. "Did a doctor teach you that?"

"No, a patient taught me that. A man named Eric... Well, I say man, but really he was just a kid. He was twenty-one and had lived with cystic fibrosis for many years, so even though he was technically an adult, they had him in the pediatric ICU, where I was working. I had just finished nursing school, so I was twenty-three, not much older than he was... Eric had been in and out of the hospital countless times. His parents were terrified, but they loved him so much, and they were putting up the best front they could. One night I walked into his room and his mom was there, and she kept saying 'Eric honey, as soon as you get better we're getting out of here and going straight to Disney World. You know that, right?'

" 'Yes Mom,' Eric said. 'That sounds great. You go home now. I need to rest. I love you.' So his parents left, and then Eric turned to me and said... 'You know I'm not going to Disney, right?'

" 'Yes', I said. 'I know, Eric.'

"He told me his parents weren't ready yet. He said, 'I've been trying to prepare them but it's too hard for them to accept it.' Then he grinned, and he asked me, 'How many patients do you have tonight?' I said, 'Three: you and two others.' He said 'Can you give the other two to a different nurse? This is important to me.'

"So I did, and I sat with him for 12 hours... I tried to rub his back, just as I always did. But he told me he didn't want me to touch him. 'You can sit next to me,' he said, 'but I don't want you to touch me... You're giving me too much energy, and I don't want it. It's my time to let go. So just sit with me and give me just a *little* energy.'

"So that's what I did. I was there with him as he wrote letters to old friends, old girlfriends, and his parents. I was present with him... just by sitting there with him. And I gave him *just* enough energy to finish.

"Eric died less than thirty minutes after my shift ended. Sharing that night with him had a profound effect on me. Eric was my teacher. He taught me about dying, as well as living. And he taught me that the energy we give to other people is powerful, and we can modulate it to give others what they need, to help them hold on, or to help them let go."

Lorraine paused at the end of her story, looking into Anne's watering eyes and taking her hand, which was resting idly on Jim's bedside.

"So you see, Anne? Jim's not moving his hand away because he's bothered by you, or he doesn't want to touch you. He just knows that it's his time. And your energy, Anne, the *love* that you share with him, it's *so, so* strong that *just* by holding his hand, you're keeping him alive. If he's moving away, it's because he's no longer afraid. It's because part of him knows it's... time to let go."

Anne was so moved by Lorraine's story that she was unable to hold back her tears. Lorraine hugged her tightly, and Anne wept in her arms.

After Anne went to bed, Jim started to mumble and moan in his sleep. Patty seemed concerned, so Lorraine offered to stick around while she finished up her notes. "I'll just be present with him and listen for a little while." Patty was thankful for the company. "That would be nice," she said. "I'm not going to be able to sleep anyway." Patty offered Lorraine a cup of tea and they sat together, sipping from their mugs while a fire crackled in the fireplace.

"That was a beautiful story you told," Patty said. "I think it really helped set my mom's mind at ease... Is that how you got into Compassionate Touch and everything else?"

"That was where my journey began, yes. I mean, there I was, twenty-three years old and in the second year of my nursing career, but already I learned one of the most important lessons, that energy is essential. Eric inspired me to learn more about holistic energy and the energy field. A lot of my interests really took hold that night."

"Well, now I feel like you're *my* teacher," Patty said. Lorraine smiled bashfully. "I mean it," Patty insisted, "You really should teach."

Lorraine smiled. "I really would love to, but I don't know if I could balance it with my hospice work... Then again, who knows? Maybe one day I will have the opportunity. Like you said, there's a plan for all of us, right?"

Just then, Jim mumbled in his sleep again, like he was trying to say something.

Patty shook her head. "He's been talking like that every once in a while. I can't tell what he's saying, and even when I *can* make out the words, none of it seems to make any sense."

"Lots of people talk like that near the end," Lorraine said. "Sometimes it sounds like nonsense. But sometimes, it really is magic."

Intrigued, Patty sat forward in her chair. Lorraine laughed, shaking her head. "I don't want to bore you with another story."

"No, it doesn't bore me at all!" Patty protested. "I love hearing your stories. You've seen so much. I feel privileged to get to hear bits and pieces of it."

"Only if you're sure," Lorraine said, relenting. She put her laptop aside and began her tale.

* * *

"About a year ago, I visited the home of an old man. He was ninety years old, a recent widower, and he was actively dying at this point. Nobody expected him to make it through the night. He had some family by his bedside, but at most, there were maybe... six people there. Two of his nieces, a couple of grandkids, and myself. Well, the old man was in bed, semi-conscious, dying. And suddenly, he opened his eyes and looked all around the room. He seemed baffled at first. 'Why are there so many people here?' he asked. 'There must be thirty of you!'

"The five or six of us standing around the bed all looked at each other and smiled. His grandchildren stifled a couple of laughs. 'Thirty people? Who is he counting??' They asked. And they started joking around. 'I think *somebody's* had a little too much morphine...'

"But despite this apparent delusion, the old man spoke quite clearly and matter-of-factly. 'Well, I don't need *thirty people* crowding around my bed,' he said. 'I'm not *going* anywhere *yet,* you know. Not before Uncle Bernie.' The family looked at each other, confused. The old man was apparently referring to his son-in-law, who everyone in the family called Uncle Bernie. 'You're waiting for Uncle Bernie to visit you before you go?' They asked. '*No,*' he said, 'I'm waiting for Uncle Bernie to *die.*' This was even odder, considering that Uncle Bernie was a fifty year old man with no obvious health problems. But before the family could even respond, the old man started to laugh and shake his head while pointing at the ceiling, as if he were having an amusing disagreement with somebody hovering directly above his bed. 'No, no,' he said. 'Listen my Dear. I give you my word, I will gather my top hat, my coat, and my shoes on schedule, and I'll depart just as soon as Uncle Bernie dies, and not a moment before.' Then he shook his head, closed his eyes, and promptly fell asleep.

"Now, the old man did not die that night. Or the next day, or the next. Three days later he passed. When I went to pronounce him, his family greeted me at the door, laughing in awe. They told me that their Uncle Bernie *had died the previous day* of a sudden heart attack, despite having no previous medical history. And although they were shaken by his unexpected death and by the immediate passing of the old man the following day, they couldn't help but laugh and shake their heads in wonder.

"I was completely awed by this. And not because this wild story was so unique, but because this sort of thing is so common! I told this story to a neighbor of mine. He's a college professor who teaches the philosophy of death and dying. He told me that the Uncle Bernie story was a tale as old as time. He even gave me a book written in the eighteen-hundreds by a writer named Francis Cobbe called *The Peak In Darien.'* It probes all these riddles of life and death... And here's the thing: There have been *thousands* of recorded incidents just like this, both modern and ancient. It's something that's fascinated people since... probably the beginning of time. Philosophers, doctors, priests... So many of them have similar stories to share."

Patty shook her head in disbelief. "That's extraordinary. I can hardly believe it, but... I also *do* believe it. Have you ever seen something like that before?"

"You know, I've been a nurse for forty years now, and a hospice nurse for the last ten, dealing with patients who are near the end. And most of them, I would say, are not afraid. Most of them have accepted what is inevitable. Most are at peace. But just because they are quiet and sometimes medicated and sometimes at peace, don't get the impression that this last bit of twilight is boring for them or uneventful. Because at the end of life, the veil between this world and the next is the thinnest. And sometimes it gives people wisdom, vision, incredible insight… It really makes you wonder. Is it possible that for a brief moment, they can see the strings that keep us all connected, the forces that hold this world together? Is it possible that those whose lives hover right between life and death, sometimes get a glimpse of whatever lies beyond? "

* * *

It was late at night now, and Jim was finally sound asleep. His breaths were calm and even. The only sound in the den was the crackle of the fire on the hearth. Lorraine had finished filling out Jim's chart, so she started to gather her things to leave. But as she rose to her feet, she noticed that Patty looked like she had left something unsaid. Lorraine gestured for Patty to say whatever was on her mind, but Patty only shook her head, not sure where to begin.

"It's just so strange, you know?" Patty said, looking sadly at her father. "Sitting, waiting, *planning* for him to die. You know, I don't want him to leave us any sooner than he has to, but… the waiting can be so hard. All this *anxious stillness*…"

Lorraine nodded sympathetically, patting her shoulder. "I know. I know it feels awful. And I'm so sorry. But the fact that you have all this time... to process and prepare, to bring your family together and speak with him before he's gone... It really is a gift. I know how that sounds, I know where you're coming from. Sometimes you wish death just happened in the blink of an eye. One day they're happy and healthy, the next day they're gone. But believe me, when you lose somebody in an instant, you'd do anything to have the sort of time you're getting with your father right now."

Patty could somehow sense that Lorraine was speaking from personal experience. Lorraine had shared things before, stories and lessons from her time as a nurse, but this was different. Patty wasn't quite sure how she knew this; but she could feel a subtle shift in Lorraine's energy, as if she was releasing something from deep within.

"Have you ever had that kind of loss?" Patty asked.

Lorraine nodded slowly, but before she could reply, Patty blurted out an apology. "Sorry if that's way too personal," she said, red in the face. "You met us all at such a vulnerable moment, and now I've just gotten so comfortable talking with you about death and loss that... Sometimes I forget you're my dad's nurse."

"No, I understand," Lorraine assured her. "And I'm happy that you feel like you can speak openly to me. You know, usually I don't like to talk about my personal life when I'm working, but with you, I'm comfortable enough to tell you... I *have* lost someone suddenly, someone very close to me. Death is always hard no matter how it goes, but when you lose someone you love without any warning... I wouldn't wish that on anyone." Patty nodded, trying to absorb this message, not sure if Lorraine would elaborate further. And then she did.

"His name was Robbie," Lorraine said. "My son. He was only three years old."

Patty looked up at Lorraine in disbelief, overwhelmed with sympathy. "Oh, Lorraine… I'm so, so sorry for your loss. How did you ever survive that?"

Lorraine sighed, reaching out and touching Patty's hand. "Somehow we manage. We find a way forward… I did. And I know in my heart that your family will find their way too."

Patty nodded, holding back tears as the two women turned to look at Jim, sleeping peacefully in the hospital bed in the den.

Chapter Twelve

Saying Goodbye

Jimmy was up early that morning, waiting for Kylee to call and say that she had landed. Although his father was still sleeping, Jimmy combed his hair and changed him into his favorite shirt: a Mickey Mantle jersey. He was looking down at his dad, remembering all the times he'd seen his father wear that shirt, when Kylee texted. Jimmy headed to the airport to pick her up.

The rest of the family stayed with Jim while Brandy rested her head on the foot of the bed. Patty quietly said to Peter, "I've been counting his breaths. They're beginning to decrease." They looked at one another with a sadness that neither of them had ever known.

Anne put her hand over Jim's, but again he moved it away. Patty reminded her of what Lorraine had taught them. "Your energy is keeping him here. He's ready to leave us, Mom." They hugged and began to cry. When Patty regained her composure, she whispered in her dad's ear, "Kylee and Jimmy are on their way, Dad, please hang on a little longer," As she leaned over to kiss him, a tear ran down her cheek.

A few minutes later, Jim turned his head towards Anne, opened his eyes for the last time, and took his final breath. Patty checked for a pulse, then shook her head.

Anne cried out, "Oh, Honey! No!" Her knees buckled and she collapsed into Peter's arms, sobbing uncontrollably. Jim was not only her husband; he was her best friend. Patty and Peter knew at that moment that their mother's life would never be the same. Nothing could ever fill that void.

Kylee and Jimmy walked into the house just half an hour after their father's passing. At first they were devastated that they had missed Jim's final moments, but their siblings comforted them. "Dad loves you so much," they said. "You were there for all of the important moments of his life. You already gave him a better goodbye than you would have been able to in the last couple of days."

Peter placed the call to Lorraine to tell her of his father's passing. When Lorraine arrived, she hugged each of them as she made her way to Jim's bedside. There she found Anne, stretched across the bed, weeping. Lorraine calmly reached out her hand and laid it on Anne's back, sharing her compassion through touch. Anne stopped quivering and slowly regained her breath. A minute passed while Lorraine simply stood there in silence with them. Then she slowly took her stethoscope out of her nursing bag and took note of the time, officially pronouncing Jim's death.

Anne's tears had slowed to a stop, and although she looked momentarily composed, Lorraine knew that she was probably in a bit of shock. She sniffled and looked down at her husband, and shook her head in disbelief. Lorraine placed a hand on her arm.

"Let me freshen him up. You can stay, or step away and take a moment if you'd like," Lorraine offered gently. Kylee took her mother by the arm, and escorted her towards the kitchen.

* * *

Shanice the social worker arrived a few minutes later. She gathered with the family in the kitchen, offering her sincere condolences to each of them. All of Jim's children softly thanked her, still quietly processing this solemn procession of events. But Anne shook her head, her eyes still wide with worry. "Do we have to call Jim's doctor now? Somebody should call him, right? And the funeral director? I can't remember the phone number. I know Jim wrote it somewhere..." Shanice understood how she was feeling. Anne was still in search of a practical outlet for her anxiety, a way to channel all her worries and fears into an actionable to-do list. So Shanice comforted her just as Lorraine had done moments earlier.

"Don't worry," she said. "That's what I'm here for, to guide you through all of that. I'll call the funeral director as soon as you're ready. Things will move quickly once we put in the call, so for now, just take whatever time you need. Say whatever you need to say."

"I don't know what to say," sighed Anne. "I never thought this day would come...I'm just not ready to let him go. I don't even know where to begin."

"Sometimes people like to say a prayer, or read something. I had a patient named Ginny who wrote a poem as she was dying, and she asked me to read it at her funeral... But you don't *need* to do anything. Whatever serves you and your family. Say your goodbyes if you'd like, or just take a moment to breathe and be present with him. This will be the last time you'll all be in the home together with Jim."

As this realization dawned on Jim's children, a wave of sadness filled the room. A silent tear spilled down Kylee's cheek. Peter choked back an audible cry. Not knowing where to begin, Jimmy turned to Shanice and said, "That poem that your patient wrote… Do you have it? Maybe you could read it for us."

Shanice nodded. She pulled her phone from her pocket. After searching for a brief moment, she began to read:

Lift the veil so that I may see
beyond the limitations of this physical world
calming the cries of my heart and illusions of my mind
allow me to let go of my attachment to form and embrace formlessness,
securing my connection to my loved ones.

Deep in my soul is a place of knowing
that passing from this Earth dimension only means end of form.
I remember that our souls are connected, through all eternity, time and space.
As this truth rises up in my being it brings me a sense of peace and comfort
opening a divine connection with my loved ones that death can never erase
Thank you for helping me remember that life is everlasting
By the grace of God it is so.

* * *

There is no playbook for a final vigil. Every death is different, each goodbye unique. And while death touches all of humankind, while every person who walks this earth shall one day pass from it, we have never developed a uniform script for how to say goodbye. No matter how much we can anticipate a death, we often feel caught off guard in the moment of departure. Sometimes the wise words we may have memorized or the traditions we've carried for generations suddenly evade us, and we are left with a profound inability to find the right parting words. And yet somehow, we find a way to say goodbye, a way to let go.

Kylee was the first to move back into the den, where she sat by her father's bedside alone. Peter thought he heard her crying. He followed her in there to comfort and assure her. He didn't want her to feel guilty for not being there at the moment of Jim's death. But as he got closer, he saw that despite the tears still drying on her cheeks, she wasn't crying. She was *laughing.*

"I don't know why," she said, "but I can't help but laugh. I just keep thinking about our quiet, reserved father, who used to *crank up* the volume on the stereo and *blast* Tchaikovsky…"

She giggled and Peter joined in with her. "Yeah," he said, "The 1812 Overture." Kylee laughed, nodding. "-- to the point where all of the windows of the house shook when the cannons blasted. Must have really shocked the neighbors."

At the sound of their laughter, the rest of the family drifted back into the den. And with no playbook to follow, no script to read from, they each began to say their goodbyes.

Patty talked about how their father used to take them on those long drives in the car, stopping at the roadside stands for apples or ice cream. Somehow they always wound up on the road adjacent to the airport, where they used to watch the small planes take off and land.

Jimmy recalled their days at Yankee Stadium, where his dad would talk about the times that he went there with *his* father, and how they used to talk about seeing Babe Ruth, Lou Gehrig, Yogi Berra, Mickey Mantle…

Peter talked about the year that he and his father turned their basement into a family room. They had spent so much time planning and creating something that they were proud to say they had worked on together. "Measure twice, cut once," his father had always said. Peter would never forget that. Nor would he forget his father's love of flying, that his father had passed that love onto him like a torch, and that his father was so proud when Peter got his pilot's license, "even though we *did* have to keep that from Mom," Peter said with a smirk.

Kylee remembered all of the wisdom and advice her Dad had always given her when it came to her job. Her dad and her had always found ways to help each other. And she'd never forget the things that were most important to him: the Sunday family dinners, the vacations, the time they spent together. He was all about family.

Anne recalled the look on her husband's face whenever he talked about his time in the Air Force. She spoke dreamily of their extended honeymoon on the beach in Biloxi, Mississippi. And with a quivering lip, she added "And I loved how he smiled at me whenever I talked about Derek Jeter. He knew how much I loved watching him play." With a slight smile on her face, she added, "Derek was my

Number Two…your father will always be my Number One."

Anne's children grinned at their parents' old joke. Finally, Anne took a deep breath and concluded their informal eulogies. "He was the best husband, the best father, the best man I've ever known." She turned to her daughters sitting on either side of her. They were each holding her hand.

Patty looked around at her family. Instinctively, without acknowledging it, all of them had reached out for one another and taken each other's hands, forming a circle around their father's bedside. After a moment of silence, Patty began to pray out loud. "Our Father, who art in heaven…" And although she had prepared to say the prayer alone, the rest of the family joined in, their soft voices filling the room in unison. There was a silence after they each said "Amen."

Kylee wiped a tear from her eye and hugged her sister. "Thank you, Patty. It has been so long…maybe never…that we've all prayed together as a family."

* * *

Shanice and Lorraine re-entered the room. Peter turned to them. "Should we call the funeral director now?"

Shanice reiterated what she had said earlier. "There's no rush. This is your time. I can call the funeral home when you're ready. Just let me know when that time is, and I will make the call once Lorraine and I have left."

Anne replied, "You can call them now. That extra time is just what we needed."

A little later, the Funeral Director and his assistant arrived. Lorraine led the family to the kitchen, leaving the Funeral Director to prepare the body. Shanice spoke to the family. "I made sure to tell them everything that you wanted, and the funeral home will go over it with you again, and make sure that it all happens according to your wishes. I'll give you a call tomorrow to discuss our bereavement services."

"I don't think I need it, Lorraine," Anne said. "I do have my family."

"Of course. And maybe you won't need it right away, but a week or a month from now, it could help to have emotional support. Either way, we're here for you."

As the funeral director took Jim's body from the home, Shanice and Lorraine began to depart. Patty hugged them both. She looked at Lorraine with a tear in her eye. "You and your team have gone through this entire end-of-life process with us. And not just the nursing, but your stories, your Therapeutic Touch, your spiritual knowledge, and your friendship… We just couldn't be more grateful for everything that the whole hospice team has done."

Lorraine hugged Patty once again, said her goodbyes, and left the house with Shanice, closing the door behind her.

Epilogue
A Tribute To The Fallen

Through the most difficult of times, the family appreciated the constant support of the hospice team. The hospital bed and the oxygen tank were taken away, the leftover medicine disposed of. Suddenly all of the signs that their house had become a hospice center in Jim's final months faded, and their home began to return to normal, or whatever their new normal was. In coordination with Shanice, the funeral director had prepared everything just as the family wished. A nondenominational minister was brought in to perform the funeral service and the US Air Force Honor Guard would be there to represent the time that Jim spent in the military. The only thing left to do was to gather pictures to commemorate Jim's life. Patty took on the responsibility as she had always been the family photographer, a hobby that she had picked up from her dad.

Over the last few months, the family had put aside any differences in order to focus on Jim and Anne… but now it was all eyes on Anne. During the next two days, Anne's children delivered meals and spent as much time with their mother as they could. When the family gathered at the dinner table for the first time without Jim, Anne surprised everyone by sitting in Jim's old seat. And although this was unfamiliar, in some ways it diminished the anguish her children might feel at the sight of their father's empty chair. It was also Anne's subtle way of declaring that she would try to face this new chapter of her life head-on, a chapter in which she alone was seated at the head of the family table.

* * *

On the night of the wake, Anne arrived at the funeral home escorted by her two sons, her daughters entering behind her. Jimmy and Peter stood at the entrance, admiring the photos that Patty had put together. The pictures told a story of happier times, and they brought a smile to everyone's face. Anne turned from the collection of photos to the flag-draped casket at the far end of the room. And to her children's surprise, she began to move towards it alone... Although she could barely find her feet, she knew that she had to face his casket now, or she would fear this solemn act for the rest of the evening. She knelt before her husband's casket. She was silent for a while, until her children heard her crying and speaking softly. When she was finished, they were there to help her to her feet.

After a few minutes the rest of the guests began to arrive to pay their respects. The family had waited to tell their neighbors and Jim's old friends about his passing until after they had told all of their extended family, so this was the first time Anne had seen or heard from many of her dear friends and neighbors since his death. The sight of old friends and the warm embrace of the community did much to lighten her heart, even at this somber moment.

* * *

The following morning, Anne woke up with a pit of despair. It was the day of Jim's funeral, time for the family to say their final goodbyes. However somber the mood was during the service, the Pastor gave a beautiful homily to recognize Jim's life and commitment to his family and service to the country. The Pastor then asked if anyone wished to say a few words about Jim. Kylee immediately stood up and spoke of the wonderful life that Jim and Anne had given their children. She even repeated a few of Jim's famous stories, regaling them with tales of his time in the Air Force, romantic descriptions of his first dates with Anne. The crowd was moved by Kylee's words. She represented her siblings well, and Anne was so proud that she even mustered a smile through her tears. As the service came to a close, the sound of a bugle playing taps filled the air, and everyone turned to the Air Force Honor Guard, who played the song beautifully, sending waves of emotion through the room. The Honor Guard stoically carried the casket to the crematorium, as per Jim's wishes. Although they held their heads high, Jim's entire family knew that life would never be the same for any of them.

* * *

Patty saw Lorraine on her way out of the funeral. Patty hugged her and asked Lorraine to join them for the repast. "Thank you," Lorraine said, "but you should enjoy dinner with your family. I just wanted to come and pay my respects."

"We've invited everyone to come," Patty said, "Please. I insist."

Lorraine nodded warmly. "Of course. I would love to join you."

Patty smiled. "Plus," she said, "I already miss our talks."

"Me too," said Lorraine. "Shanice has been filling me in on how you guys have been doing with the funeral and everything, but I wanted to be here myself."

"Oh Shanice has been wonderful," Patty said. "She's been such a helpful resource throughout all of the planning, and she's been telling us about bereavement counseling and everything. I'm hopeful that my mom will go. When she's ready."

"That's really good to hear."

"And how have you been doing?" Patty asked Lorraine.

"I'm doing well actually. And I have you to thank... You know how you've always been telling me I should teach Reiki and holistic medicine to other doctors and nurses? Well, you must have put some good energy out there, because suddenly the hospice organization I work for had the same idea... We're going to start training staff in the Fall. Thank you for giving me the confidence to pursue that," she added.

Despite how sad Patty had been all morning, now she couldn't help but grin from ear to ear. She hugged Lorraine tightly as a beam of sunlight cut through the clouds and illuminated the front of the church yard.

* * *

Everyone piled in to Jim's favorite restaurant: Anne and her children, friends, neighbors, out-of-state relatives, even a few of Jim's old Air Force buddies. Surrounded by family and friends, Anne felt lifted by a wave of love and support. She spoke with many of Jim's oldest friends and his doctor, who they had always been close to. Before Anne sat down for dinner, her neighbor Ryan came up to her and gave her a great big hug. He asked her how she was feeling, and told her how much Jim had meant to him.

"You know he convinced me to come out to my mom," Ryan said. "I don't know if I would have worked up the courage without him. He really changed my life." Anne was touched and surprised to hear that Jim had had such a positive impact on their young neighbor. As if to prove it, Ryan turned and pointed to a handsome young man who was talking with Ryan's mother on the other side of the room. "That's Ian, my boyfriend. If it weren't for your husband, I never would have brought him here with me today. And I'm really glad I did."

* * *

Peter made the first toast. "We all knew and loved my father," he said. "And we all know that if he were here right now... He'd be leaning against *that* wall in the back of the restaurant with his arms folded across his chest until my mom told him it was time to socialize." Everyone laughed. Jim's party demeanor was a long-running joke on both Anne and Jim's sides of the family.

"But if you joined him for a second, away from all the noise, he'd also be the first one to engage you in a really great talk. He had so much love and respect for everyone here. And as Kylee said today, the love he had for his family was endless…" By the end of Peter's speech, the room was full of misty eyes and the sound of laughter. There was a marathon of toasts over dinner, and everyone who raised a glass spoke lovingly of Jim, their friend, their neighbor, their CPA, their Air Force Captain, their baseball coach, their patient, their husband, their father. Hearing Jim spoken of so well did Anne's heart some good. That evening, everyone could feel his energy filling the room, lifting each of them up.

* * *

Life went on. Anne's children still came over for dinner, and she had visitors several times a week. On weekends she would take Mikayla to the beach or the playground or the aquarium. Whenever Ryan was back home next door, he would come over in the mornings holding two thermoses of coffee, and they would walk the dog together. Brandy, who had never slept in bed with Anne before, began to curl up next to her on Jim's side of the bed every night. Life went on, but it was a quieter life. People told Anne to join a class. Take up painting or ballroom dancing or join the community board, they'd say.

But outside of a few neighbors and her family, Anne didn't feel much like socializing. Patty had been trying to convince her to join bereavement counseling, but Anne had been avoiding it for some time. Perhaps a bit of Jim's "I don't need any help" attitude had rubbed off on her after all. And for now, this quiet little life felt appropriate.

Then one morning, Anne woke up earlier than usual. Since Jim had passed, she'd been sleeping in till the late morning. The rest felt good, and with nobody there to wake her up with the smell of coffee, she rarely felt like leaping out of bed first thing in the morning. But today was different. It felt like something was nudging her, lifting her out of the bed. She could almost hear Jim's voice in her head: *"C'mon Anne,"* the voice said, *"We've got places to be."* So Anne got dressed and left the house, even though she didn't know what those places were.

She drove, not really thinking about where she was going. Maybe she would swing by the grocery store, pick up a few things. Her list was smaller these days. One bag of frozen vegetables, not two. A pint of 'half and half', not a quart… But she found herself driving past the grocery store and got on the highway.

She passed the exit for Patty's house, and Peter's. She passed by the exit for the church where Jim had been laid to rest. She kept driving until she found herself pulling into a parking lot, looking up at the entrance for the hospice center. And then she remembered that today was Wednesday, and that Patty had scheduled her to begin bereavement counseling group therapy today. She had written the date on the calendar, but she never seriously thought about going. And now she was here. It was as if something had brought her here, carrying her on the wind.

She was early. The therapy session wouldn't begin for another half an hour… Maybe she would just turn around and go home. She could always come back another day…

But instead, Anne got out of the car and walked towards a park bench across from the hospice center. The bench was sitting in a patch of sunlight, and the warmth felt good on her face. She looked across the lot, and that's when she saw a familiar face. Lorraine was leaving the hospice center. She looked happy and full of energy, and her face lit up at the sign of Anne.

Lorraine approached the park bench and the two women gave each other a big hug.

"Anne! How are you?" Lorraine asked excitedly.

"Wow, it's so good running into you here! Were you working today?" Anne asks.

"Yes, but not with patients," Lorraine said. "Lately I've been working with the hospice board. We're developing a training program for nurses and other hospice staff who are interested in learning Reiki and Therapeutic Touch... I've always wanted to do something like this, but your daughter Patty was actually the one who inspired me to start the program."

"That's Patty for you," Anne said, smiling. "She's the one who wanted me to come here today."

"You're here for the bereavement counselling?"

"I guess so..." Anne said. "The truth is, I still don't know if I'm ready to talk about it... Sometimes someone will see me in the grocery store and they'll ask me how I am, and I never know what I'm supposed to say. They don't know what to say either. So they usually just say something like; *I'm sorry for your loss*' or '*the Lord works in mysterious ways;*' or '*At least you have your children...*' Nobody really understands how much he meant to me. Except for maybe my kids.

But they have their own grief, and I don't want to burden them with my own..." Anne sighed. "It's just difficult to talk about. I've heard that it's an important part of letting go, but maybe that's what I'm afraid of, letting go."

Lorraine nodded thoughtfully. "I understand that. And in some ways, you know, we never really *do* let go..."

Anne reached out and touched Lorraine's hand, remembering something. "Patty told me that you lost a son..."

Lorraine looked down. She opened her purse and fumbled through it, looking for something. Maybe a tissue, Anne thought.

"I'm sorry to have brought that up," Anne said. "I know how hard it is to talk about. It's hard for me, anyway..." Lorraine looked up and Anne was surprised to see that she wasn't upset. In fact, she was smiling as she opened her wallet and took out a photograph.

"No. No, I love talking about Robbie. He was such a happy little boy. Every time I look at this picture it brings a smile to my face." She handed it over to Anne. A single glance at the picture almost broke Anne's heart.

It was a photo of a sweet little boy, his white blond hair stuffed under a construction hat. He wore a jean jacket over a t-shirt that bore an image of a tiny windsurfer. He was smiling brightly, his blue eyes twinkling in the sun. He was looking at someone off camera, giving them a big cheerful thumbs-up.

"He's beautiful," Anne said, tears filling her eyes.

"He is. And he looks just like his little brother. Jimi, my windsurfer."

"Your other son is a windsurfer?" Anne asked. Her brow furrowed as she looked back down at the photo, confirming what she noticed earlier: Robbie's t-shirt had a windsurfer on it.

"You noticed the shirt?" Lorraine asked, grinning. "I always carried this photo in my wallet but I never really noticed the windsurfer on Robbie's shirt, not for years and years. Not until the night my son Jimi won his first windsurfing competition. We were on a boat that night, leaving the competition, when a surprisingly strong gust of wind blew my purse right over. My wallet tumbled out of my purse. And that photo slid right out in front of me. For the first time, that little detail leapt out at me... The windsurfer. That wind that blew my purse over... Jimi had that *same wind* in his sails that day. It was a gift from his big brother. A sign that he was watching over us."

Anne shook her head in awe. "Such a beautiful story. And I believe that you're right. It was a sign. A gift." Anne handed the photograph back to Lorraine, realizing something. Here she was, worried that she would never be able to live a full life without Jim by her side. And yet here sat Lorraine, living proof that it was possible to find your way forward through even the darkest of times.

"Lorraine," Anne said. "When we first met, I always felt like you were kind of... magic somehow. Like you had some secret reserve of strength I couldn't see, or I didn't know where it came from... Like your compassion for the dying and those left behind, it was more than just kindness or professional courtesy. It seemed... *learned* somehow.

After losing Jim sometimes I thought -- sometimes I *still* think: how will I carry on? You know? But losing a child... I can't begin to imagine how you ever came back from something like that." There was a pause, and then Anne asked Lorraine, "How... *do* you come back from that?"

Lorraine sighed and reached out her hand, placing it over Anne's.

"Anne, we do our best. We love them, we are loved by them, and we go on faith that somewhere, some day, we'll meet again. Until then, we carry them with us. And in those moments where we don't have the strength, when we're full of despair and we've lost the wind in our sails, just close your eyes and remember them, and all the ways they touched our hearts. And when we do that, we can *still feel them*. Touching us, holding us, lifting us. Because when we carry them with us, we are never alone. They carry *us* with *them*, too."

* * *

Lorraine and Anne parted ways shortly thereafter. As Lorraine walked to her car, a breeze stirred up a rainbow of fall leaves behind her. Anne turned once more to the hospice center and saw that someone was holding a door open for her and for others just like her... And although they were all the way across the parking lot, Anne could tell that they were smiling.

This book is dedicated to my son Robbie (1987-1990).
My love for him is endless.
He will never be forgotten and
will always be in that special place
in my heart and
"in my pocket"…

And to my youngest son Jimi who has lived his life to the fullest
and lives every day in the present moment.
His love of life and the water has brought me so much
peace, joy, and love.
He understands what I do
and has supported me throughout his life,
and I am forever grateful.

ACKNOWLEDGMENTS

My deepest thanks again to Patty Alviggi and my editor Danny Whalen for helping me tell this story. Without their patience, their compassionate and insightful storytelling, and their tireless work, I never would have been able to write this book.

I would like to acknowledge the high caliber expertise and professionalism of East End Hospice. I am so proud to be a member of this organization. Special thanks to Angela Byrns, Children's Bereavement Coordinator and to Mary Crosby, President and CEO.

I am so blessed to have my brother, Stuart Whalen, who never gives up on me, always has my back, and has been there to guide and support me throughout my life and this book.

My deepest gratitude to my patient Vinetta and her husband, Mark. Their love for one another and faith opened their hearts to find the one last thing that they needed; a God-given sign. I'd also like to thank my patient Franco Biscardi for teaching me how to live and love more deeply. And a very special thanks to Virginia McEvoy, a hospice patient who wrote the poem included in this book.

Deepest thanks to Michael Kaplan, MD, a compassionate doctor. His presence alone brings healing and understanding to all.

Heartfelt thanks to Marianne Gelber, MSN, ACHPN, whose expansive knowledge of medicine for patients' comfort, along with her compassion, is unsurpassed.

I'm appreciative of Susan Steiner, OTR/L, CST-D, who teaches CranioSacral Therapy worldwide for the Upledger Institute International. She has inspired me to deepen my Therapeutic Touch and CranioSacral knowledge and practice.

Thank you to my neighbor, Stephen Manning, and our many conversations on the subject of 'death and dying.'

Thanks to Dr. Michelle Peal, who has always been there for me with her spiritual support.

This book was inspired by Susan Cotta after reading her book, *I Can Show You I Care: Compassionate Touch for Children.*

Many thanks to Deb Heneghan, who helped with the first go-around of this book. We appreciated all of your input and edits.

Thank you to the Shinnecock Nation; for their people and the care shown to the loved ones within their community.

Special thanks to our extended team of our local police, EMS and firefighters who assist us whenever called upon.

Thanks to my many colleagues and good friends for always listening and finding meaning in my stories.

And most of all, thank you to all of my patients and their families. It has been an honor and privilege to guide you and your loved ones in the most delicate of times.

THE HEART OF HOSPICE

Aimee Whalen

RN, Hospice Nurse,

Master Radiesthesist, Craniosacral Therapist,

Reiki Master

"Integration of spirit and medicine."